Treating
THE AGON[Y]
of Asia

Tom Dooley was the remarkable young doctor who won thousands of friends for America by healing the sick in the jungle hospitals at the edge of tomorrow.

In the remote Laotian villages of Vang Vieng and Nam Tha he built his hospitals. Within the shadow of Communist hatred he and a staff of five (three ex-Navy men and two Notre Dame students) learned how to convince people who had stoically borne pain and sickness as a part of life that they could be helped. Learned that miraculous cures could be effected if you knew when to co-operate with witch doctors. Learned what it meant when your patients were murdered outside your door by political assassins. Learned how to give the rudiments of first-aid training to native volunteers who believed only in herbs and incantations.

But more than this they learned how medical aid could reach the hearts and souls of a nation and change a people's fear and hatred into friendship and understanding.

The address of
MEDICO is:
Box 2, Times Square
New York, N. Y.

Other SIGNET Books You Will Enjoy

DELIVER US FROM EVIL
by Thomas A. Dooley, M.D.

Dr. Dooley's first book, telling of his experiences as a Navy doctor in Indo-China, where he and his shipmates fed, clothed, and treated thousands of refugees and helped them escape to freedom.   (#D1992—50c)

THE NIGHT THEY BURNED THE MOUNTAIN
by Thomas A. Dooley, M.D.

Dr. Dooley's account of the founding of his second jungle hospital, the growth of his organization MED'CO, and the beginning of his own gallant fight against cancer.
(#D1974—50c)

OUT OF MY LIFE AND THOUGHT
by Albert Schweitzer

Remarkable autobiography of a great medical missionary and religious leader. With Post-Script 1932-1949 by Everett Skillings.
(#MD83—60c)

THE DELIVERANCE OF SISTER CECILIA
by William Brinkley

The suspenseful, true-life story of a courageous nun's flight from the Communists.
(#D1420—60c)

The
EDGE
OF
TOMORROW
by
Thomas A. Dooley, M.D.

A SIGNET BOOK
Published by **THE NEW AMERICAN LIBRARY**

THOMAS A. DOOLEY, M.D.
1927-1961
(*The New York Times,* Thursday, January 19, 1961)

Dr. Thomas Dooley, the medical missionary, died here last night at Memorial Hospital. Death by cancer, which he had calmly awaited for two years, came at 9:40 P.M.

Dr. Dooley, famed for his work in establishing hospitals in Laos, was thirty-four years old Tuesday. He was visited then by Cardinal Spellman, who said yesterday:

"I tried to assure him that in his thirty-four years he had done what very few have done in the allotted scriptural life span."

The patient also received hundreds of birthday messages, including a telegram from President Eisenhower.

"It must be a source of heartened gratification," the President said, "to realize that in so few years you have accomplished so much for the good of distant peoples and have inspired so many others to work for all humanity."

Dr. Dooley underwent surgery for chest cancer at Memorial Hospital in 1959, but returned to his work in Laos, although he knew that the disease was likely to recur. He was forced to return to Memorial Hospital last month.

In an article written for *The New York Times Magazine* in 1958, Dr. Dooley summed up his work in Laos as follows:

"I believe that it behooves those of us who attempt to aid in a foreign land to be content with small achievements. We must not attempt to build dynasties. We must try to build at the level of the people, or just one step ahead, always planning it so that the Asian can ultimately take over."

The statement reflected the will of the author but not his driving personality. The physician not only was a medical missionary but also an author, lecturer, gadabout and indefatigable promoter. In five years, starting with his medical work among refugees streaming from Communist-held North Vietnam in 1954, the often brash young doctor achieved international fame.

By 1960 a Gallup Poll showed that he was one of the ten most admired Americans.

He agreed with his critics that he practiced "nineteenth-century medicine" in his remote jungle hospitals in northern Laos a few miles from the Chinese border. By that, Dr. Dooley meant that despite such modern drugs as penicillin, his style of medicine was relatively simple compared with present-day techniques in this country. The various young American volunteers who worked with him in Laos did not have medical degrees.

Dr. Dooley was the driving force behind Medico, an organization that collects funds and sends medical teams to establish hospitals and clinics in the world's least developed countries.

He was credited with personally raising $850,000 for Medico. He made lecture tours, appeared on television and promoted Medico constantly, traveling to this country from his Laos base many times. In addition, he turned over royalties from his best-selling books for Medico programs.

Thomas Anthony Dooley III was born January 17, 1927, in St. Louis, one of five brothers. In 1944 he entered the University of Notre Dame but dropped out to enter the Navy as a hospital corpsman. After the war he went back to Notre Dame and eventually received his medical degree at St. Louis University in 1953.

In the Navy again in 1954, he was serving as a volunteer medical officer in the Vietnam area at the time that former French colony was partitioned into Communist and non-Communist areas. Dr. Dooley's care for nearly 600,000 refugees from the Communist area won acclaim. The Navy awarded him the Legion of Merit. And *The Washington Post* in an editorial said of his refugee work: "It was the ultimate example of effective person-to-person contact with a foreign people."

Dr. Dooley's best-selling book, *Deliver Us from Evil*, was based on his experience in caring for the 600,000 refugees in camps at Haiphong. He was a Navy lieutenant (j.g.) at the time.

Home again in 1956, he resigned from the Navy and, with three medical corpsmen who had worked with him at Haiphong, returned to the Far East to set up a hospital in Laos.

He described it as a small village hospital on stilts. It was at Nam Tha. The Laotian government supplied canoes to transport equipment. In 1958 Dr. Dooley turned over the hospital to Laotians and established a new one twenty miles across the mountains at Muong Sing. He also had planned a third hospital in Laos.

Dr. Dooley also wrote *The Edge of Tomorrow* and *The Night They Burned the Mountain,* based on his Laotian experiences. He held the highest national decoration of South Vietnam and was the first American to be decorated by the Kingdom of Laos. He also received the highest Laotian medal —the Order of a Million Elephants and the White Parasol.

Universally admired in the United States, Dr. Dooley was a controversial figure among Americans working in the Far East. Physicians criticized him as a "hit-and-run" doctor who gave snap diagnoses and was absent from his hospital too often. Many complained of an overbearing ego and said he was insensitive to the feelings of others. Laotian children revered him, and before his illness he often roughhoused with them.

As for his ego, Dr. Dooley once said: "After all, like most humble Irishmen, I think I'm practically faultless."

In 1959 he fell and bumped his chest. Later he felt a growing lump in his chest. It was diagnosed as sarcoma, a fast-spreading cancer. He flew to New York for a successful operation for removal of the malignancy. Weeks later he was back on the job in Laos. But he was afflicted anew with a serious ailment in his vertebrae.

At Hong Kong in December, 1960, he was fitted with a steel-and-leather harness stretching from his shoulders to his hips. He called it his "iron maiden."

Dr. Dooley, a bachelor, is survived by his mother, Mrs. Agnes Dooley, and two brothers, Malcolm and Edward. At his death his mother was en route to her home in St. Louis. The funeral will take place there.

FOREWORD

This, the true story of six young Americans, takes place in an exotic land of tinkling wind bells and clashing cymbals, half a world away—the Royal Kingdom of Laos.

This is not a document of figures and facts, nor is it to be taken as a historical narrative. It is not a generalization, nor is it fiction. It is a true story of six Americans who formed a fellowship with the people of Laos, and indeed with many other people throughout the world, as you will soon see. At the start I would like to tell you about the concept of this fellowship, and about the man who conceived it.

Since my earliest days in medical school the work of Doctor Albert Schweitzer has been one of the great inspirations of my life. To enter into correspondence with him was a cause of great satisfaction to me. And the biggest thrill of all occurred recently when I visited the great old gentleman himself. It is difficult to describe him. He has sensitiveness and forcefulness at one and the same time. He is both tender and majestic. His grizzly old face is wonderful to see.

One of Doctor Schweitzer's most important concepts is that of the Fellowship of Those Who Bear the Mark of Pain. I and my men have found this Fellowship wherever we have gone. Who are its members? Doctor Schweitzer believes the members are those who have learned by experience what physical pain and bodily anguish mean. These people, all over the world, are united by a secret bond. He who has been delivered from pain must not think he is now free, at liberty to continue his life and forget his sickness. He is a man whose eyes are opened. He now has a duty to help others in their battles with pain and anguish. He must help to bring to others the deliverance which he himself knows.

Under this Fellowship come not only those who were formerly sick, but those who are related to sufferers, and whom does this not include? On the members of this Fellowship rests the humanitarian task of providing medical help to the "have-nots" of the world. Dr. Schweitzer believes that men of medicine should go forth among the miserable in far-off lands and do what has to be done, in the name of God and Man.

In a very small way, because of my profession, I have found entrance into this Fellowship. I have discovered hundreds of others in it, too. Many people all over the world heard of our mission to Laos. Thousands wrote to us, many offered gifts, and some offered useful suggestions. Others volunteered to come and work with us. One man even sent me a detailed outline of a Community Development Plan that he had used in South Africa forty years before. These people were all members of that Fellowship, even though they didn't realize it.

The list of things that were sent to me would bring tears and smiles. There were a few foolish things, some useless ones. But the greatest part were wonderful, and desperately needed. The only repayment I can think of is the simple utterance of gratitude.

The help of the schools was perhaps the warmest of all. Dozens of schools wrote and asked what they could do, so we tried to give each a project. Franklin School Three, in Passaic, New Jersey, sent hundreds of bars of soap that they had collected. Their teacher, Miss Mary Kennedy, suggested that each student write me a letter. My mail was already hitting about two hundred and fifty letters per month, but the grade-school children's letters were most appreciated. One little fellow wrote that he stayed with his father at a New York hotel and while there he talked the maid out of a "whole suitcase full of hotel soap." The soap was important because in the mountains of Laos there is none, nor is there any kind of substitute. We would give a couple of bars of "sabu" to each skin case that came to sick-call.

Freemont Junior High in Anaheim, California, sent me nearly five hundred pounds of soap, every ounce of which was put to use. Many doctors and nurses sent me sample-size medicines that the pharmaceutical houses pass out. I had plenty of the basic antibiotics, but these assortments were just the thing for an odd case here and there.

The Irish nuns of St. John's Hospital in St. Louis, Missouri, have no idea of how much one nurse "borrowed" from them. She even sent me a spinal anesthesia tray that I needed, with a note saying that the anesthesiologist helped her make up the tray. Another nurse, Clare McCartney of Santa Barbara, sent me over thirty boxes of medicines, samples of drugs for everything from nausea to nose-bleeds. To have people so far away take such a personal interest in my mission reminded us that we were not alone.

A few days after the little boy Ion was operated on (see Chapter Six), I received a letter from Chaplain K. I. Rewick of Punahoe School in Honolulu. His high school students had taken up a collection and sent me several hundred dollars. We decided that this was just about the cost of the medicines and bandages that we would need for this boy, so we wrote and told them that Ion was "their" patient. We sent pictures as he progressed, and tried to keep Punahoe School up to date on his condition. Ion could not pronounce the name of the school, but he did understand that hundreds of young American boys and girls were taking care of him.

An old shipmate of mine, Larry Aggens, went on a regular Chicago Roundup program. He gave talks to raise money for us. The only time Larry took off from this program was while he was in the hospital having an injured eye treated. As soon as he got out, with a plaid eye-patch and a Hathaway shirt, he returned to his task of being beggar-in-chief of the Dooley mission.

A doctor in England sent us books on the medical problems of the tropics. Several doctors in America also sent me medical texts. Mr. Brayton Lewis of the Holliday Bookshop in New York made a point of keeping the Dooley mission up to date on new books. Monthly we received a book or two, and along with *The Saturday Review* that the Helperns sent, we were fairly *au courant* with the world of letters.

Assistant Secretary of Defense, E. Perkins McGuire, sent me several hundred dollars specifically tagged "for liquid cough medicine."

When my boys came through Hawaii on their way to Laos in September 1956, they stopped at one of the luxurious hotels on Waikiki. One evening they were greeted by three ladies who had read of our mission and of the boys' arrival, and had decided to entertain them. The boys had a great time. When they said good night, one woman offered to send the daily newspaper to Laos. The boys smiled but gave the address, and from that day until our departure "Mis" Spring sent the daily Honolulu *Star Bulletin*. It always arrived in bunches of eight or ten, but we were pretty much up to date on the news. Thanks, Mom Spring!

On a plane a few years ago, I met a Bill C. White. He was going to Mexico for a vacation from the hard labor of acquiring a college education. We talked about my planned mission and he was intensely interested. Months later, in Laos, I received a letter from him along with a box of chocolate bars. The letter was welcome, but the candy bars were true manna. I wrote and thanked him, and he kept the boxes coming for the rest of my time. Bad for the complexion, but good for the heart.

It seems that the depth of goodness and responsibility in Americans is often more apparent abroad than it is at home. This thoughtfulness quickened our pulse. A lot of good-will for America was born when we explained to the Lao the origin of the candies, baby clothes, pencils and T-shirts which we gave them.

One day we found in the mail sack a large crate which was badly beaten up. We opened it and found inside stuffed animals, drawing books, sheets of colored paper, a wild assortment of ribbons, safety pins, hair barettes and just about everything that you might find on the mezzanine floor of Macy's. We also found a note saying that this was a gift of the Morning and Afternoon Kindergartens of McKinley School, Harrisburg, Illinois. After we thanked them by mail, their teacher, Miss Mildred Walden, explained how she had heard of our work, and decided that Kindergarten was not too young for her students to begin to learn of their responsibility to other lands—a responsibility that comes to them as birthright because they had the great fortune to be born free men. I admire this woman for her desire to teach internationality to even the youngest. There is no need to worry about the quality of education with teachers like her.

We sent some polaroid pictures of her children's box-in-action. She said that one little girl commented: "Look, Miss Walden, that child has the stuffed horse I brought to school for the Box for Laos." If this is not foreign aid on a person-to-person basis, what is?

One day I received a dollar bill in the mail. It was from a blind girl, Aurora Lee, who lived in Thailand. She had read

The Reader's Digest Braille edition of my book, *Deliver Us from Evil*. Later she heard that we were in Laos and wanted to help. Somehow she found an American dollar and sent it on to us. Mrs. Iva Gordon of Timberville, Virginia, saw a picture of us in a newspaper and thought we looked crummy. She sent us two pairs of khakis and shirts per person. They were well received; I guess we did look crummy.

The Rotarians of Hong Kong sent us a check, as did the Rotarians of Honolulu. The Hawaiian Residents' Association sent us 475 pounds of roller bandages. Admiral Stump transported them to Saigon for us. In cubic measurement this load was the equivalent content of about one box car. Gestures like this illustrate to Asians that Americans can project beyond national boundaries the generous and kindly impulses which are so characteristic of them.

The Basilians, a Catholic Youth Organization in Los Angeles, wrote that they wanted to send something for the four of us. I explained how I would have given an arm and a leg for some U.S. pancakes with maple syrup. Every week for the remaining sixteen months we received a box of pancake mix and a jar of syrup.

I attended Notre Dame University in the middle forties, and a good friend of mine on the staff there was Erma Koyna. When I was in Viet Nam, she sent things to my refugee camp. In Laos, hardly a month passed that I did not receive something from her. If she did not directly buy the gifts, then she bamboozled the poor salesmen who came to the University. The salesmen ended up sending a crate of lollypops, soap, candy bars, and the like.

I was able to extend my mission beyond the planned six months because my money was holding out through the kindness of my friends. And how many hundreds of hours of prayers were offered around the world for Dooley and his boys? This was an everflowing fountain of encouragement for us. I knew my mother's prayers were the most powerful, for her love is closest to God's. And there were teachers, friends, brothers and others who were always sneaking our names into their prayers. I thought of my beloved Irish nuns at St. John's Hospital in St. Louis. While saying their prayers, brogue and all, at the feet of Our Lady, I'm sure they added: "Please take care of Doctor Tom, he's such a hothead . . ." Out on Clayton Road the Dutch nuns at St. Mary's and Desloge Hospital also wrote that I was remembered in their prayers. I once asked them to "pray like hell" for me. They wrote back that they were "praying like heaven." I have spent years working with nuns, but never really learned much about them and their singular and secret way of life. Yet I remember their goodness, the sweetness of their soap and starch, and the softness of their reprimands. Now I am learning the power of their prayers.

I received a note from a priest who had just been released from a Communist torture cell in Red China, where his hands had been crushed between two stones. He was offering a daily *Memorare* for the blessings of Jesus on us.

A little Jewish girl in school in New Jersey says that she prays for me "frequently." A priest in Cincinnati offers our name during each day's Mass. In how many churches around the world have people lighted small flickering candle flames for us? With the candles they uttered: "God, grant safety, peace and success to Tom Dooley and his boys." How grateful we are to them and to Him.

I wish I could make personal acknowledgment in these pages to each and every individual and organization (see Chapter One for an important group of these) whose help we have received. Unfortunately, I do not have enough space for that, and have only been able to cite a few examples of the many generous acts, both material and spiritual, for which we are indebted. Instead I will close with the prayer which served as our inspiration in Laos and may well stand as the epigraph of this book:

> Give us, Thy worthy children,
>   The blessings of wisdom and speech,
> And the hands and hearts of healing
>   And the lips and tongues that teach.

THOMAS A. DOOLEY, M.D.

Box 2
Times Square
New York, N. Y.

CONTENTS

1

"But I Have Promises To Keep"

High above the Pacific, flying westward in a luxury airliner, the night passes swiftly. Passengers put away their books and briefcases; one by one, the reading lights wink out. Lulled by the monotonous beat of the engines, the Honolulu-bound vacationers and the businessmen bound for Tokyo and Manila slumber peacefully.

But I am the sleepless traveler, my mind filled with memories that are more captivating than dreams. I close my eyes and recall that wretched refugee camp in Haiphong in the Spring of '55. Operation Cockroach the Navy called us —one young Navy doctor, still professionally wet-behind-the-ears; four young enlisted men who had only a few months' training as hospital corpsmen; and a half-million filthy, diseased, mutilated Asians fleeing from the godless cruelties of Communism.

That was North Viet Nam during what was ironically called the "Passage to Freedom." That was where Dooley really came of age.

How many times have I told that story? I told it not only in the pages of *Deliver Us from Evil*, but whenever and wherever I could find Americans who were willing to listen. But, at least, it was never told in vainglory. For what we *did* in dying Haiphong was far less important than what we *learned* there.

We had seen simple, tender, loving care—the crudest kind of medicine inexpertly practiced by mere boys—change a people's fear and hatred into friendship and understanding. We had witnessed the power of medical aid to reach the hearts and souls of a nation. We had seen it transform the brotherhood of man from an ideal into a reality that plain people could understand.

To me that experience was like the white light of revelation. It made me proud to be a doctor. Proud to be an American doctor who had been privileged to witness the enormous possibilities of *medical aid* in all its Christlike power and

17

simplicity. Was that why the foreign-aid planners, with their billion-dollar projects, found it difficult to understand?

I preached so ardently that my folks began to worry. "Look, Dooley," my friends would say, "you've had adventure enough. When are you going to settle down?" My mother reminded me of all the things I had always wanted, and now might have. A home, a wife, kids, a nice medical practice, maybe a few fine hunting horses. My old medical mentor told me I'd better get on with my postgraduate training if I hoped to be a good orthopedic surgeon.

How could I make them see that things would never be the same?

I remember those lines by Robert Frost that kept echoing in my mind during those fretful days:

> The woods are lovely, dark and deep,
> But I have promises to keep,
> And miles to go before I sleep.

I knew the promises I had to keep. I knew that the keeping of them would take me many miles, back to Southeast Asia, to the very edge of tomorrow, where the future might be made—or lost.

One evening in February 1956, after I had been home from Asia only a few months, I went to a dinner at the Vietnamese Embassy in Washington, D.C. This night I had a premonition that all hope of returning to Indo-China with a medical team of my own would hinge on whatever happened at that dinner.

Regretfully, I was aware that I could not go back to Viet Nam. The north was now locked behind the Bamboo Curtain. I was not needed in the south where the medical teams of the Filipinos' Operation Brotherhood were already doing a wonderful job. Where else could I operate and utilize my knowledge of Indo-China? Cambodia? Laos? Would I, as an American, be welcome there in view of the ticklish political situation?

To help me find an answer to these questions, my good friend, Ambassador Tran Van Chuong of Viet Nam, had arranged a dinner party for me to which he had invited a number of Cambodian and Laotian diplomats. Late that evening I was still talking about the kind of medical mission I had in mind—small, privately financed (mostly out of my own pocket), without any government or church sponsorship or obligations. The team would consist only of myself and a few of the young Americans who had served with me in North Viet Nam.

We would be plain Americans working among the plain people of the country, wherever we were needed, in paddy fields and villages, in jungles and mountains. Perhaps, if we did a good job, we might inspire other Americans, doctors and laymen, to follow our example of international cooperation on a people-to-people basis.

The Cambodians listened, politely non-committal. But I saw that the Laotian ambassador, the Hon. Ourot Souvannavong, was following me with keen interest.

"But, Dr. Dooley," he asked, "why should you, a young man just released from your naval duty, with a career before you, choose to make this sacrifice? Obviously, you have much to offer. But what do you stand to gain?"

Once more, I tried to explain my deep conviction that medical aid, offered on a people-to-people basis, could form lasting bonds of friendship between East and West. If this was true, we American doctors had a duty to perform. Since I had served in Southeast Asia and had seen the need, the duty for me as an individual was inescapable. Besides, I was young, unattached, free to go wherever I was needed.

Suddenly, I remembered something that big, hardboiled Boatswain's Mate Norman Baker had once said in answer to a somewhat similar question. Gambling on my ability to translate Baker's homespun American into French, I explained how Baker had groped for words to explain our motives, and then blurted out:

"Aw, hell, sir, we just want to do what we can for people who ain't got it so good!"

The Cambodians raised their eyebrows and smiled—Baker's words had hit the mark. But Ambassador Souvannavong beamed, and from the way he shook his head in frank admiration I could practically read his mind: These incredible Americans!

"Dr. Dooley," he said, "my country would be honored to reecive your mission. Will you come to see me at the Embassy in the morning?"

The following day, seated in his study, the Ambassador gave me a briefing on social and political conditions in the Kingdom of Laos. He began by telling me why medical teams like mine were needed there. For the entire population of about two million, he said, Laos had only *one* doctor who was a medical graduate by western standards. He watched my astonishment with a sad smile.

"Oh, we have a few young men we call *médecins indo-chinois*," he added. "They are graduates of the *lycée* who have had a little medical training. But for the vast majority of our sick people there are only the witch doctors and the sorceress." (The *lycée* is roughly equivalent to an American junior high school.)

Then the Ambassador explained that the one doctor in Laos was his nephew, Dr. Oudom Souvannavong, who was also the Minister of Health. "I am sure he will welcome you, and give you all the help you need," he said. "And I must warn you, Doctor, that you will need help and guidance. You will find everything in my country difficult, possibly dangerous."

We stood before a huge wall map, and the landlocked Kingdom of Laos, which extends down the middle of the Indo-China peninsula, reminded me of a long bony finger, with the huge knuckle attached to the red hand of China and the fingertip poking into Cambodia and South Viet Nam.

Ambassador Souvannavong pointed to the northwest province bordering on China and Burma. For the first time I noticed a name that was to haunt me—Nam Tha.

"If you go up here, where you will be needed most," he said, "you may face considerable danger. Nam Tha is isolated, the people are poor, disease is rampant. The political situation is delicate—very difficult for a Westerner to understand."

I looked at the map, and was struck by the fact that Nam Tha lies almost on a straight line due west of the tragic city of Haiphong in North Viet Nam—perhaps 500 miles as the vulture flies. The two adjoining provinces had become the temporary haven of the Communist-led Pathet Lao under the terms laid down by the Geneva Conference of 1954—the same conference that had partitioned Viet Nam and committed Cambodia and Laos to a "neutralized" status in Indo-China.

I said we were willing to take our chances, but I also promised to be discreet. Ambassador Souvannavong shook my hand warmly, and assured me that he had confidence in me.

"Many times before," he said, "white men have come to help us. But always they had other motives—colonization, trade, even our religious conversion. I really believe your motive is purely humanitarian. That will make your mission unique in my country," he said. Then, with a twinkle in his eye, he added: "And, also, for some of my people, a trifle hard to believe."

To give my mission legal status, Angier Biddle Duke, president of the International Rescue Committee, arranged to have us taken under the aegis of the IRC, which enjoys worldwide respect. I took another look at the bank account in which I had been salting away the proceeds from my book and lecture tour, and said a prayer. Then, profiting by my experience in Viet Nam, I again made the rounds of the pharmaceutical companies and surgical supply houses with my hat in hand.

Their understanding and generosity overwhelmed me. The Charles Pfizer Company gave me over $100,000 worth of antibiotics. Johnson & Johnson supplied bandages and surgical dressings. The A. S. Aloe Company of St. Louis, Mo., donated a complete line of surgical instruments and equipment, and the Aloe employees passed the hat and presented me with a handsome check!

The Mead Johnson Company gave me a bill of lading for a huge supply of vitamins and protein extract, and Mr. Johnson wrote out his personal check for $5,000. Walt Disney presented us with a sound projector and a collection of Disney movies for the children of Laos. The Willys Company presented us with a jeep, especially constructed for rough-country operation. (We later named the vehicle Agnes, after my mother.)

I went to Abercrombie & Fitch in New York and ordered a lot of essential equipment—cookstoves, lanterns, sleeping bags, etc. The bill was staggering. When the salesman learned the nature of my mission, he excused himself and disappeared into a vice-president's office. He came back with the bill slashed to a fraction of the original amount.

One day in Washington, D.C., I was waiting to testify at a hearing of the International Rescue Committee concerning free Viet Nam's role in Asia today. A dynamic little woman, who was very late, sat down beside me in the last row and whispered, "Has Doctor Dooley given his speech yet?" I smiled and said, "No, but he should be great." She nodded and said, "I have been chasing that man halfway around the country." "Why?" "I want to give him five thousand pounds of protein." At that moment I was called as the next speaker. We met afterwards in the corridor and it turned out that she was the affable Miss Florence Rose, executive secretary of the Meals for Millions Foundation. She did give me five thousand pounds of their multi-purpose food, which was directly responsible for saving hundreds of lives in my mountain hospital during the following year.

The U. S. Navy did not let me down. They agreed to transport the tons of medicines, food and equipment that I had accumulated, even though I was now a civilian. They transferred this for me to South Viet Nam, at a tremendous saving to my mission.

I spent several weeks going in and out of the various American agencies in Washington concerned with work in Asia. The International Cooperation Administration promised me a great deal, sincerely and genuinely, but the end result coming from their men-on-the-scene in Laos, turned out to be very little. However, I.C.A. in Washington helped me greatly in the earlier planning stages. So did the United States Information Agency, which pledged a battery-run tape recorder.

During this period I met Mrs. Raymond Clapper, widow of the famous war correspondent killed in Korea. Mrs. Clapper is the head of the CARE offices in Washington, D.C. By guiding my steps, introducing me to people, and just being a good friend, Mrs. Clapper became a sort of midwife to the birth of Operation Laos of the International Rescue Committee. (Incidentally, CARE has an excellent midwife kit, in appearance much like the flight bags which air travelers carry; it was Mrs. Clapper's idea that CARE donate about fifty kits to the graduates of the midwife classes that I planned to inaugurate. Later in my story you will learn the good use to which they were put.)

But I had left the most difficult phase of the plan—lining up my men—until the last. All along I had been counting on Norman Baker, Peter Kessey, and Dennis Shepard, the most devoted and dependable of the enlisted men who had been with me in North Viet Nam. This wasn't going to be easy. Denny Shepard, newly married, was taking his pre-med at the University of Oregon. Pete Kessey was attending pharmacy school in Austin, Texas. Baker, also a bridegroom, was still in the Navy. Would they as civilians return to that part of Asia where they had seen such wretchedness?

However, Pete and Denny responded to my call promptly and enthusiastically. Baker's ship was somewhere at sea; several weeks passed before I could get in touch with him. Then one day, in Washington, I received a long-distance call from Baker in San Diego. When I told him about Operation Laos, his roar could be heard from coast to coast, even without the help of AT&T.

"What! Back to Indo-China? Are you crazy? Why, you slave-driving fool—sir—you couldn't pay me to go back into that hellhole! Besides, my wife wouldn't stand for it! Hell, no —not a chance!"

There was an awkward silence. I just let him simmer down. Then. . . .

"Hello . . . You still there, Doc? Listen, you don't really need *me,* do you? What makes you think we can do any real good out there? And there's something you seem to have forgotten. (*Hearty chuckle.*) Little Old Baker is still the pride and joy of Uncle Sam's Navy!"

I assured him that I needed him, that Operation Laos was one helluva big challenge, and that I was pretty sure I could get him out of the Navy on an early discharge. I could hear him grumbling and moaning.

"Aw, whatthehell, Doc, sure, I *volunteer!* But Priscilla's going to divorce me for this, sure as shootin'!"

(Bless her heart, Priscilla Baker did nothing of the sort. She went right ahead with a project I didn't know about at the time—having their baby.)

In July, 1956, after a short seven months in America, I started on my return trip to Asia. I lectured in Hawaii, Japan, Hong Kong, and then flew to the Philippines to speak with the founders of Operation Brotherhood. From them I could glean much for my own mission, for we had really borrowed the whole idea of non-governmental, non-sectarian medical service to foreign nations from this Filipino endeavor.

My men followed behind me, and we were to meet in the Philippines.

On a sweltering day in August I stood in the Manila airport watching a plane glide down through the heat haze rising from the runway. It taxied around, and the door swung open. Out stepped Pete Kessey, our lean and hungry looking Texan, followed by 200-pound barrel-chested Baker (flexing his muscles, as always), and then quiet, serious Denny Shepard. How very young they looked! Pete and Denny were 25. Baker was still only 21. Yet they were more mature and dependable than most men twice their age.

We had about an hour's wait before leaving for Saigon, which was to be our "staging area." The boys plied me with questions. What kind of gear did we have? How had I ever high-pressured the Navy into hauling the four tons of stuff to Saigon? Where did we go from there? What kind of place was Laos? ("Yeah, man," groaned Baker. "I can see now that this means living on C-rations and holding 24-hour sick-call!")

When we were back aboard the plane, the talk turned serious. I got out my map and explained that, if my plans went through, we would operate up north in the province of Nam Tha. Denny gave a long, low whistle of surprise. He had a bundle of notes and clippings, and knew as much about Laos as I did.

I told them about the flying trip I had made to Hong Kong to meet Oden Meeker, a dynamic young American, who had served in Laos with CARE during the famine of 1954. Oden strongly favored the plan to operate in Nam Tha. It was a critical area, he said, the most isolated part of Laos, and politically the most vulnerable. "Those mountain people have rarely seen a white man," said Oden. "They have no allegiance to the central government. They're just ripe for the Commie treatment."

The boys listened solemnly. Then Baker said: "Look, Doc, you've got to level with us. What are the odds on this setup? I'm a married man now. So is Denny. Fact is, Priscilla's going to have a baby. Besides, I never did like the sound of those Chinese prison camps!"

Well, I said, the odds were about standard for that part of the world. No better, no worse. We'd been in tough spots before, but we had done our jobs, and come through with our hides intact. Baker hooted.

"Oh, we sure did—only you forget that we had the U. S. Navy back of us last time!"

I let that pass, and switched to the kind of job we had to do. We wouldn't be "showing the flag" so much this time, as we had in Haiphong; we'd be showing American face to a lot of Asians who had been told that American white-men didn't give a damn. I reminded them of what we had learned in Haiphong, and invited them to think of what we could accomplish by working among people on the village level in Laos.

Pete Kessey spoke up. "Doc, it looks to me like you expect to accomplish an awful lot in a short time. You know we only signed on for six months. You think we can do a job by then? And what happens to you when we pull out?"

That was the one part of the plan that had me worried,

but I couldn't admit it. After six months, I said, I'd be able to play it by ear. I told them about the *médecins indochinois*. Maybe I could train a few young Lao to serve as assistants. And I also had a scheme in mind for getting a few replacements from the States.

They sensed that I was whistling in the dark. Baker declared that this was the screwiest part of the whole setup. Pete just shook his head. I was glad when Denny Shepard broke it up.

"This is one devil of a time to be talking about going home," he said. "We're not even there yet!"

2

Arrival in Laos

The huge Vietnamese cargo plane made three trips from Saigon to Vientiane with our four tons of crates and packing cases. We went in on the last flight, made a perilous landing on the steel-mat runway, and climbed down bone-tired after six hours perched atop packing cases. While a small army of coolies unloaded, we piled our essential gear into an antiquated truck and headed into town. The jeep named Agnes was driven across Cambodia, Thailand, and north to Laos on an unbelievable ten-day trip. It was floated across the river on a sampan, and finally arrived at Vientiane.

Vientiane, laid out by the French as the colonial capital of Laos, has broad avenues lined with huge teak and acacia trees. But when we arrived the monsoon rains had turned these unpaved boulevards into rivers of mud, crowded with ancient automobiles, oxcarts, pedestrians, wandering buffalo and sleepy dogs. Signs of the ending of the French colonial period were everywhere. Paint peeled from buildings in huge patches, there were buffalo wallows on the lawns of the National Assembly, and the caretaker's wife had hung out her laundry along the elaborate colonnades.

When we pulled up before the new Samboun Hotel we had a minor but revealing mishap. The brand new concrete pavement collapsed under the truck's weight, and the front and rear wheels on the right side sank hub-deep in the ditch, pitching everything to starboard.

We climbed out and surveyed the damage; the Laotian driver just shrugged and said, "Bau pinh yanh." We soon learned that this is a common expression in Laos. It means something between "Well, never mind" and "The hell with it." Two days later the broken-down truck still stood in front of the hotel, listing to starboard in the ditch. *Bau pinh yanh!*

The first and second class rooms of the hotel were not yet ready for occupancy, so we were lodged in the "slave quarters." These servants' rooms were small but clean, and of course they had never been occupied by slaves!

26

While the boys supervised the warehousing of supplies, I hustled over to the U. S. Embassy to pay my respects to Ambassador J. Graham Parsons. The visit was brief and formal. I detected a coolness in Ambassador Parsons' manner. Dooley's "unofficial" mission, apparently, wasn't very popular in official circles! In fact, I was later to learn that in the eyes of most Americans in Laos, Dooley was "annoyingly autonomous."

Then I went to the Ministry of Health and gave my name to the receptionist. A few minutes later a handsome, energetic young man, about 35 years old, popped into the reception room and came toward me with hands outstretched. This was Dr. Oudom Souvannavong, the only doctor of medicine in Laos, and certainly the most unministerial Minister of Health I have ever met.

He escorted me into his private office, spoke glowingly of my book, and told me of the high esteem in which I was held by his uncle, the Ambassador to the U.S. Then, with these pleasantries out of the way, his manner changed suddenly.

"Tell me, *mon docteur*," he asked suspiciously, "why have you *really* come to Laos?"

For the next ten minutes he questioned me sharply. What was my connection with the U. S. Government? Was I still a naval officer? Why had the Navy transported my supplies to Saigon? Was I an agent of the CIA or any other intelligence service? What was my religion? Did I represent any Catholic missionary society?

At first I was flabbergasted, then I struggled to keep my Irish temper under control. (Much later, I learned that suspicion of foreigners was prevalent in Laos at the time.) I answered his questions candidly, perhaps a trifle sharply. At last, he began to smile again, apparently satisfied that I was neither a spy nor a Jesuit in disguise.

He knew that I was interested in the north, and I enlarged upon this. As I told him, "From a medical point of view there are tribes in the mountains whose health is wretched. From a political point of view, these people have no real allegiance to the central government of your country. From my personal point of view, there are sick people there and furthermore people who had been flooded with potent draughts of anti-Western propaganda from Red China."

I told the Minister that in conversations with his uncle in America it was thought that the place most in need was the northern Province of Nam Tha. I re-emphasized that I wished to work for the Lao government and any allegiance that I might win through medicine would be directed to the Royal Lao Government. I wished to be part of their Ministry of Health.

Dr. Oudom replied: "I have heard of your wishes to go to the north. There are many hazards there, isolation, the precariousness of border life, Communist banditry, the monsoon rain's fury, the lack of transportation." He reminded me how unknown the white man was, and how superstitious and sometimes hostile the primitive people of this foothill world of the Himalayas could be. But the Minister had cleared his conscience with necessary warnings, and now realized our determination to work where we felt the need was greatest in spite of risks.

"Frankly, *mon docteur*," he said at last, "it pleases me greatly that you are willing to take your medicine to these most wretched of our people. You have our complete approval. But, first, I must ask you to get the approval of the American Ambassador."

This request, after all the emphasis on my independent status, amazed me. But Dr. Oudom was adamant. Reluctantly, I headed for the American Embassy, feeling pretty sure that I was in for trouble.

Ambassador Parsons was emphatic in opposing my plan to go to Nam Tha. Indeed, he wanted my team to stay as far away from the China border as possible. The political situation in Laos was touchy; conditions in the north might even become explosive. No matter what I did or said or even could prove, it was inevitable that people would suspect me of being an American espionage agent. (How true, I thought—remembering Dr. Oudom.) Certainly, in the north the Communists would do everything possible to spread the word that I was a spy. While he conceded my right to go anywhere in the country that the Lao government would permit, he pointed out that if I or any of my men became involved in an "incident," the entire American position in Laos would be jeopardized.

"To go into the north at this time," he insisted, "would be extremely unwise, Dr. Dooley. I must ask you to reconsider the matter."

So, that was that! Ambassador Parsons did not forbid me to go to Nam Tha, but he certainly would not approve my going. By withholding his approval, he vetoed the plan, in view of Dr. Oudom's terms. I completely disagreed with him. In retrospect, I'm afraid I disagreed with him vehemently and somewhat brashly.

I asked him where he thought my team might operate. Without a moment's hesitation, he replied that there was scarcely any part of the Kingdom of Laos where medical aid was not needed. We went over to the map, and he indicated the area around Vang Vieng, about 120 miles north of the capital but still far south of the China border. During the Indo-China war, he said, Vang Vieng had been captured by the Communists; conditions there were still pretty bad.

Crestfallen, I went back to the Ministry of Health and told Dr. Oudom that Nam Tha was out—for the time being, at least. To my amazement, he agreed completely with the American Ambassador! He also concurred in Ambassador Parsons' choice of Vang Vieng. Health conditions were deplorable there, he said. The town had a medical aid station, but no doctor, nurse, drugs or equipment.

"You can perform a real service in Vang Vieng," he assured me.

So Vang Vieng it was. Back in the slave quarters of the Samboun Hotel, the boys heard the news with dismay. I had other things to worry about. This change of plans was going to cut deeply into my slim bankroll. Most of our equipment was designed for the mountainous north, rather than for the jungles and lowlands of Vang Vieng. Even our pharmaceuticals were intended primarily for diseases we would encounter up north.

Baker listened to my lamentations and said: "Oh, well, Doc—*bau pinh yanh!*" (Actually, when we finally did get to Nam Tha many months later, I was humbly grateful to Ambassador Parsons and Dr. Oudom for insisting upon a "shakedown cruise" in Vang Vieng.)

I now thought of Oden Meeker. Through Mrs. Clapper's introduction I had had a chance to meet the dynamic Meeker in Hong Kong. He is the young author of *The Little World of Laos*, a Lao veteran, having spent time there during the famine of 1954. Oden Meeker knows misery well. Through CARE, thousands of pounds of rice and salt were dropped from airplanes over the famine area bringing relief to thousands. While at lunch with Oden, the name of the province of Nam Tha had come up. Oden was one of the few to have ever been there and he corroborated all the Ambassador said about white men rarely being seen there. This added to my determination to take my team to Nam Tha. Incidentally, from Hong Kong I had flown on to the Philippines, where I was met by Oscar Arellano, and Amelito Mutuc. They are the founders of Operation Brotherhood, the Filipino Medical Unit whose teams are scattered throughout South Viet Nam. It is easy to understand why the Filipinos hold their heads so highly. They seem doubly proud to walk as free men. These people are on the "offensive" for democracy. They do not just sit around denying what the Communists say of us but rather they get out there and do something about it. Oscar Arellano says that each of his team members are "walkie-talkies for democracy." He said to me one afternoon, "When a man's head is empty and his stomach empty, his democracy will also be empty." To do their part as men born in freedom to help their fellow Asians, Operation Brotherhood was inaugurated as a vast medical relief program in South Viet Nam. The Philippines are the first of the nations of Asia to extend help to other nations.

Now at the Samboun Hotel in Laos, I had the first chance to glance over some of the papers that Oscar Arellano had given me on the history of Operation Brotherhood. In them I found this wonderful statement by Amelito Mutuc: "I would like to rally all young men who are earnest about life. I should like to arouse civic consciousness amongst people. I should like to instill in them the acceptance of the responsibility to work for the common whole, to free them from bias and prejudice and create in them the sincere desire to understand and to cooperate with people of other creeds and other loyalties . . . I am sure that there is a vast reservoir of talent and zeal in the region of Asia in the persons of young men of action whose devotion and dedication to service, to the community, nation and world, I can avail of without reservation."

That night in Vientiane, to get away from our worries, the boys and I went sightseeing. Strolling through the city we found a Laotian "love court" going on and squatted down in the audience. I had often heard of this unique Lao entertainment which chants of the art of courtship. It is sheer poetry, improvised on the spot. The boy extols the beauty, grace, virtue of the courted maiden; the girl sings of the boy's nobility, charm, bravery. The audience listens raptly, applauding an inspired passage with an enthusiasm that Americans reserve for touchdowns or home runs.

But I had something else in mind. We needed an interpreter. Baker and I both spoke French fluently, and Pete and Denny had a working knowledge of it. What I wanted was a dependable man or boy who understood the Laotian dialects and could translate into French. Squatting in the love-court audience, I decided to begin the search then and there.

"What is this performance?" I asked loudly in French. "What is the meaning of these words and gestures?"

The people turned and stared at me. Then a voice said: *"Moi parler français, monsieur."* He introduced himself as Chai, and proceeded to interpret the love poetry into passable French.

Chai was a short, husky lad with beautifully modeled features, wide-set eyes, clear bronze skin, and jet-black hair. He wore the native sarong, knotted at the waist, an immaculate white shirt with French cuffs (the colonial influence) and, of course, no shoes. I remember noticing his short, stubby fingers. I didn't realize that they would one day serve me expertly across the surgical table.

When the love court ended, we introduced ourselves more formally. Chai was a graduate of the Vientiane *lycée*, and apparently had a natural flair for languages. I explained that I was a doctor, and that we were going to Vang Vieng. When I said we needed an interpreter, he accepted the job enthusiastically. He claimed to know all about Vang Vieng where he had *parentage*—which we would call kinfolk or kissin' cousins.

A few days later we piled into jeeps and started to make a reconnoitering trip to Vang Vieng, 120 miles north. I asked Chai if he knew the trail. *"Oui, mon docteur."* Did he think it would be passable? *"Oui, mon docteur."* Later, I discovered that Chai was not a liar; he was just congenitally unable to say no.

For the next five hours, under blazing sun, we crept and crawled through dense jungle, plowed through monsoon mud, and hit long stretches of suffocating dust. But we also saw some of the most fantastically beautiful scenery on earth.

When we reached the cool, swift, inviting Nam Lick River, we parked the jeeps, shucked our clothes, and soon were splashing in the green water. Everyone, that is, but Chai. We looked around, and saw him sitting forlornly on the river bank.

Baker went over to the embankment, had a long conversation with the kid, and then came back grinning from ear to ear.

"For Pete's sake, don't laugh, Doc," he said. "He can swim all right. But he just ain't been checked out by the phantom that runs this river!"

I thought Baker must be kidding. But when I had dried myself and dressed, I sat down beside Chai and learned that it was all true. Buddhism in Laos has a strong admixture of ancient animism; and for people like Chai there are more spirits and phantoms in Laos than there are fairies and leprechauns in Ireland.

"This phantom of Nam Lick has taken many lives," Chai assured me. "But when we return to Vientiane I shall make an offering, then I can swim in the Nam Lick without fear."

Sure enough, a few days later, Chai plunged into the river and swam and splashed with the rest of us. He had gone to the Buddhist temple in Vientiane, made his offering, and had been "checked out" by the monk for swimming in the Nam Lick. Chai even had a talisman or charm, which he now wore tied to his wrist with a cotton string, to prove it.

We learned something else about Chai: he would not kill anything. Later when patients paid me for an operation with a live chicken or duck, Chai could not kill the birds for our dinner. However, he was resourceful in many ways and he solved the problem neatly by finding a pagan, a Kha tribesman or a villager, who was delighted to twist the bird's neck for a few cents! What about fishing, a sport which Chai loved? Wasn't this killing, we asked him. *"Non, mon docteur,* I merely take the fish out of water. It it dies, that is not my fault. I have not killed it."* We were aware that Chai represented a fairly high standard of life in Laos. Though born a peasant, he had received a *lycée* education, spoke fair French, and was a bright lad in all respects. If Chai was so bound by the world of spirits and phantoms, how strongly must the totally ignorant people of the kingdom be dominated by them. What obstacles would this create in our practice of medicine?

That first night was spent in the hut of the chief of a village half way along the road. Here was the first chance that we had to sit around a villager's house and converse. We were amazed and frightened at the tenacity with which these primitive people clung to their world of phantoms. How bound they were by the despotism of good and evil spirits, white and black magic.

The next day we drove through more staggering, luxuriant jungle until nightfall.

We had seen absolutely no sign of life along this trail for several hours, and the sight of the sleepy village of Vang Vieng seemed to us a haven.

The setting for Vang Vieng must have been selected by a master artist. It is spectacular. The village rests at the foot of stupendous walls of rock, rising two thousand and three thousand feet into the sky. These mountains have no foothills. There's no gradual rise or slope. Just an absolutely flat plain; then suddenly, abruptly, a staggering wall of rock. The tops of these mountains are covered with pine and on the side walls stubby trees grow out of the rock at painful angles and reach upwards for light. The tributary of the Mekong River winds around the mountains in search of lowlands. There are many stories of this river's perils, stories of deadly leeches, parasites, huge fish, rays and snakes, as well as Chai's stories of spirits and dragons.

The broad river pays no attention to the road. There were several places along this trail where large bridges were necessary and hundreds of places where smaller ones were needed. In the dry season floating bridges or small planks suffice, but when the rains come these are all washed away. Hence, the road is unusable for six months of the year. Even during the dry season, which starts in September, the 120 miles from Vientiane to Vang Vieng took two days.

3

Sick-Call at Vang Vieng

Thanks chiefly to one elderly member of Chai's *parentage*, whom the boys irreverently named Ojisan (Japanese for "old man"), about half the people of Vang Vieng were out to meet us when the trucks and jeeps of Operation Laos arrived in town. Ojisan had spread the word that we were white medicine-men bringing powerful remedies to the people. Hence many of the women and children came with gifts of flowers, cucumbers and oranges.

We found the Lao dispensary at one end of the square (actually the area surrounding the town well) directly across from the home of the Chao Muong or mayor. It was a low, whitewashed building of three rooms. Since it had no living quarters, Ojisan gave us a house which he owned at the southern end of the town.

Norman Baker was our chief construction man, in the best Seabee tradition; and under his direction the boys went to work converting the dispensary into a small hospital. They swept, swabbed, disinfected, and then whitewashed. With the aid of a half-dozen coolies, we cleared the surrounding yard (which was to serve as our "reception room") of debris, cow dung, and heaps of foul bandages and dressings. Then we built a fence to keep out the wandering water buffalo.

The medical supplies were uncrated, and the boys did an ingenious job of converting the empty boxes into tables and benches, and cabinets in which to store our pharmaceuticals. Then we borrowed some cots from the local detachment of the Royal Lao army. When these had been deloused and repaired, we set them up in one room which was to serve as the ward.

Our living quarters presented a tougher problem. Ojisan's house was a typical Lao hut perched six feet above the ground on stout poles surrounded by a "porch" and reached by a steep ladder. We climbed up, took one look inside, and came out shuddering. The place was filthy.

The boys tore out everything inside the hut including the

bamboo partition between the two rooms. They swept the ceiling clear of soot, cobwebs, and rats' nests, then went to work on the walls. When this accumulation of ancient crud had been swept out, they hauled up buckets of river water, broke out boxes of soap-powder and bleach, and swabbed the deck Navy-style.

The villagers presented us with woven bamboo mats for floor covering, and we laid out our bedrolls and hung mosquito netting. Then we installed all the packing-crate bookcases, benches and tables, and placed two cots against the wall as lounges. This would be our "living room."

Pete Kessey insisted that even the poorest white trash back in Texas wouldn't live in such a place. Maybe so. But, at least, no one could ever say that the men of Operation Laos lived apart from the natives in an air-conditioned "American compound."

We never announced sick-call, and we needed no publicity. Only a few days after our arrival we were awakened one morning by sounds that were to become a familiar part of every dawn—the howls of sickly babies, the hacking coughs of tubercular mothers. Why wait on line at the hospital, when you can camp on the doctor's front porch!

Frankly, I was overwhelmed by the horrible health conditions we found in Vang Vieng. These were yaws, tuberculosis, pneumonia, malaria and diseases far more heartrending. I was appalled by the sight of so many women mutilated and crippled in childbirth, and by many traumatic injuries long neglected and horribly infected.

The hideous yaws we could cure with the "1-2-3 treatment" —one shot of penicillin, two bars of soap, and three days! There was little we could do about the tuberculosis, except to control the paroxysms of coughing with cough syrup; for it is the wracking cough that frequently causes pneumonia and hastens the tubercular's death.

One of the most horrible diseases for us to treat was leprosy. Here the patients who gaped at us were just remnants of human beings, rotted and bloated beyond ordinary shape. In dealing with this loathsome disease I had constantly to suppress the strong urge of nausea.

More than 50 per cent of the patients we saw had malaria. Usually these people had survived many attacks of the disease, and achieved a certain immunity; but they were left with greatly enlarged spleens. When the spleen is diseased, the blood loses some of its ability to coagulate, and the slightest cut or bruise can cause a serious hemorrhage. So we pumped vitamins into almost every patient we saw.

One morning at sick-call a poor woman pushed a huge, smelly bundle of rags into my arms. I peeled away the layers of clothing and uncovered a baby about a year old. It was a hideous sight. The abdomen looked like an overblown balloon that was about to burst, the chest looked like a miniature birdcage. There was a tiny monkey face with wild, unseeing eyes. Kwashiorkor's disease! And this was only the first of countless cases we were to encounter in Laos.

Kwashiorkor's disease, fairly common among backward people in the tropics, is not caused by infection but by ignorance. It is the grotesque result of malnutrition. Metabolism fails, muscles waste away, liver and spleen are enlarged, the abdomen swells, and the heart and circulation are damaged. The end result is death.

But this horrible process is reversible if caught in time. This was an extreme case. The mother had fallen ill and was unable to nurse her baby; so, from the age of about six months, the child was fed only rice and water.

Successful treatment of Kwashiorkor's disease depends upon extremely cautious feeding so as not to overtax the weakened system. We injected vitamins, and then used the wonderful protein powder called MPF (Multi-Purpose Food) supplied to us by Meals for Millions. MPF can be used in many ways. Two ounces of the powder made into a broth, for example, provide proteins equivalent to a steak dinner.

We put the baby on a diet of MPF solution and fruit juices and got remarkable results. The damage to the heart and eyes, unfortunately, was irreversible. But the child lived.

That night I told the boys that we were adding another project to our overloaded schedule. We were starting regular classes, open to all comers, in nutrition, hygiene and similar matters. There was entirely too much disease caused by ignorance in "our town." We might as well get after it now.

Every day, from dawn to high noon, we held sick-call at the hospital. In the afternoons we loaded our faithful Agnes (already showing signs of age) and held "jeep-call" in the surrounding countryside, often with Pete and Denny in charge when I was doing surgery. Then, in the evenings, the crowds would gather in front of our house for Walt Disney movies— and for our lectures on the facts of living, delivered *via* our proud interpreter, Chai.

Chai decided that he would have all the earmarks of his new

position as interpreter for the Americans. He bought himself a pair of shoes while in Vientiane, and now was a man of station. But he walked with such a painful gait that it only lasted a few days, and he was barefoot again on the soft sod of Laos. For special occasions he put them on again, but these were rare and painful moments.

Sick-call was always an ordeal; for, aside from disease and ignorance, we had to contend with the quaint customs of the people. The line would form sometimes double, in the crowded courtyard and file into the dispensary. I would sit on a chair, with Chai beside me, and try to get the patient to sit on the bench facing me. That wasn't as easy as it sounds.

To the people, the American doctor was a "mandarin"— high on the social totem pole. (Even Chai acquired a certain nobility by association and was always addressed as *Thanh,* an honorific reserved for more important personages.) But the trouble was that, according to long established custom, the humble Laotian's head could never be higher than the mandarin's. Consequently, when examining a patient, I was forced to bend or squat lower and lower. Sometimes I had to grovel on the dirt floor in order to listen to a heartbeat!

We also had difficulty with the Lao nurses we were trying to train. These earnest, intelligent boys and girls would perform the most distasteful duties, handle any part of a filthy and diseased body. But at first we could not get them to clean a head wound, or even hold a patient's head while I stitched the scalp or pulled a tooth. The Lao believe that the spirit of Buddha resides in the head, hence even touching it is like defiling the tabernacle.

Obstetrics, if I may call it that, was our biggest problem from the outset. We estimated that about 50 per cent of the babies were lost before or during delivery. One out of every five mothers died in childbirth, and many of those who survived were left horribly mutilated.

To the Laotian midwife, the job is over once the baby is born. The child is wrapped and placed in a basket, ashes are rubbed on its forehead, and the grandfather blows into the infant's ear to impart wisdom. Meanwhile, the mother, who has given birth to her baby squatting upright on a stool, lies neglected and often hemorrhaging critically.

The care of the child's umbilical cord was another frightening spectacle. As scissors are not available, the cord is cut with two sharp pieces of bamboo. This cleanly severs the cord, but the bamboo is usually filthy. The midwife then rubs into the open end of the cord a powder made of earth and ashes. It is believed that when this is rubbed into the cord the child will absorb some of the power and strength of the trees, and the spirits of the ancestors who are buried in the soil. Ghastly as this seems from the standpoint of sterility, it is astonishing that we never saw a single case of an infected umbilicus.

Hence, we gave high priority to our midwife training program. There were about four practicing midwives in Vang Vieng when we arrived, and perhaps as many more young girls who aspired to the calling. We won them over to our side, had them help around the hospital, and made them promise to call us for each childbirth. When we went on a call, we would take along one or two of the younger girls. And, always, we carried a bag containing the wonderful midwife's kit prepared and distributed by CARE. Each of these kits contains gowns, gloves, cord ties, basins, bowls, dressings, soaps, towels, etc.,—all the essentials for the delivery of 25 babies.

We taught the girls the principles of modern, aseptic midwifery, and the importance of post-partum care of the mother, including removal of the placenta. Then, after each one had delivered 25 babies under supervision, and had proved her proficiency and dedication, she was "graduated" with appropriate ceremony, climaxed by the presentation of the CARE kit—always the bag that I personally had carried and used. (This was extremely important for "face.")

Just as in America nurses are "capped" at graduation, we "bagged" our midwives in Vang Vieng. And it worked. Those wonderful young women, armed with their CARE kits and somewhat dedicated to the aseptic principles we taught them, have removed many of the old horrors from maternity in that part of Laos.

Our practice of medicine was not confined to humans alone. One day a man came to Pete and presented the symptomatology of his friend. This friend lacked pep, was unable to hold his head up, had bad feet, and was losing weight. The man said that this syndrome came upon the friend a few weeks after he had been badly mauled by a tiger. Peter registered astonishment and inquired further, "How old is your friend?" The man had no idea. Nor could you ask how much weight he had lost, because in Laos there is no system of measurements for anything of this size. Peter asked many more questions and finally said that the man would have to bring his friend to the clinic. The man said that he had done this already; his friend was tied up outside the hospital. Peter went outside and found the friend, a small Tibetan pony, tethered to a tree. Pete called to me and I went and joined in the consultation. Indeed, the pony was in bad shape. The tiger had torn the throat and chest considerably and had slashed the forehead open. Each claw mark was infested with maggots. I sent for water, soap and cotton and proceeded to wash and clean the sores. We put some antiseptic over the wounds and then wrapped a large dressing around the horse's neck to prevent further maggot infestation. Pete rotated around each end of the horse injecting penicillin, none of us knowing the exact dosage of the antibiotic for horses. This patient came back every day looking a little better each time. Finally we discharged him from the active treatment list. It was now too late to save ourselves; the word spread and hardly a week passed that someone did not bring a horse or a water buffalo to us for treatment. The complaints were as myriad as those of the two-legged patients—bad eyes, cough, loss of weight, fever, or just senility.

One dawn we were sitting around our not-yet-completed house eating C-rations and coffee for breakfast. I glanced at the gathering of women on the front porch and was commenting to Pete about it. There were usually people there every morning, but this day there were so many they had overflowed to the front lawn. Among them was a small young lad of about twelve years old, who was not a member of the Lao race but rather was a Kha tribesman. All of the people looked bad, but this lad looked worse than any. He was squatting, shivering in the early morning coolness, draped in filthy rags. When I left the house to walk down the lane to the hospital, he got off of his haunches and said, *"Koi chep ken kenoi,"* which means, "I have a sore leg."

When I looked at the massive infection from an old cut on his leg, I wondered how on earth he could even walk. I asked him through Chai, the interpreter, how he had come to us. He said he had walked two days and two nights and had arrived at our house around midnight last night. Why did a feverish lad spend a cold and dismal night squatting outside my house? "I did not think it would be right to disturb the American mandarins while they slept."

We started immediate treatment. Under anesthesia, we slashed open the pus pockets of his legs and drained them.

We gave him penicillin and antipyretics. We did not put on any dressings but let him lie in bed on clean sheets, allowing the pus to drain out of the open tracts. Several days later we convinced him of the attractiveness and the importance of a bath in the river, which was just down the road a bit. Even with his fever, a bath was imperative.

We gave him soap and a brush and he hobbled on down and scrubbed like he has never scrubbed before in his life. He wanted to please us. My boys rewarded him by giving him one of their clean T-shirts and a pair of khaki pants, and they then gave him a fine new CARE blanket that he could keep. The Kha boy was overwhelmed. Rarely have I seen a happier boy. He spent the next ten days in our new hospital receiving antibiotics, vitamins and what American nurses call "T.L.C.," tender loving care. This is what he devoured more than anything. He liked being liked. He loved being cared for. This wistful lad had suffered a lot and deserved some happiness. He had the right to disturb us whenever he wanted to. We explained this to him repeatedly. When we discharged him he was cured of the staphyloccus infection of his leg; and cured of the more insidious poison, fear.

While we were in Laos I had a small battery-run tape recorder. I made recordings on this every week and sent them to a St. Louis radio station, KMOX. The station played them in St. Louis in hopes that people there would understand a little bit of what we were up to. I tried to tell the people who listened something of this little Kingdom of Laos, of the sadness, the chaos, the disease. I tried to tell the people in St. Louis of the children in the area of my world. I know many people in St. Louis listened to me, because they responded. One time I commented, "I certainly wish I had some hot chocolate." I should have known better; the response by mail, air freight, and other modes of transportation was overwhelming and we received hundreds upon hundreds of cans of hot chocolate. My boys commented that I should have said, "I certainly wish I had a steak sandwich and some french-fried potatoes."

The Basilian Club sent me weekly boxes of pancake mix. This started an increase in our standard of living but a decline in the lining of our stomachs. Peter decided that he would fatten the boss up and perhaps improve his disposition, so he began to prepare pancakes for our morning's breakfast. I am sure that he had never cooked a pancake before in his life. No matter how large, how small, how long or how quickly he worked, Peter's pancakes always had that same consistency —putty. Once he had some batter left over, so he decided to keep it until the next day. But on the following morning, he found he could not use it—the stuff had solidified.

Never in the thousands of hours that I had devoted to thinking about and planning for this mission in Laos did I anticipate the depths of misery in which we would have to work and eat and sleep and live. Never did anybody in the Washington briefings, in the Lao Embassy, at the Hong Kong lunch or in the refugee camps of Viet Nam adequately indicate what life would be like for us four Americans in the tropical jungles of Central Laos. I had done considerable research on Laos; back in America I scoured the public libraries, the National Geographical Society, the State Department, the United States Information Agency, and every other source that might have on hand some information on the conditions of the country in which we had chosen to work. I tried to plan my mission around the facts that I acquired in this manner. However, I was completely stunned by the conditions that existed in the village of Vang Vieng.

After a few weeks in Laos a twenty-year-old lad named "Si" joined our team. He became our housekeeper, cook, bottle-washer and handyman. Si had the features of an eleven-year-old boy and took great pride in his two gold teeth, a mark of wealth to these people. He took very loving, tender care of his Americans. Having a coolie, a cook, a houseboy, interpreters and other servants in Laos is a different thing than it is in America. We considered these people an integral part of our team, not employees. They dined with us, bathed with us, swam with us, worked with us, and came out on night-calls with us. Later they became extremely devoted to us, caring for every aspect of our life, easing the strain whenever they could. We grew to love them all very much.

Our domestic life was a life of monotony. It was the same every day—long lines of sick at the hospital, worrisome diseases, stink, and misery. The food we ate was also monotonous. Our meals were the least attractive part of our day. During our time in North Viet Nam we were lucky never to have had any serious intestinal problems except an occasional bout of dysentery. This was partly due to caution on our part and partly due to luck. Not being so sure of the latter this year, we decided to be doubly cautious. The Navy gave us a large supply of C-rations to help us in our dietary problems. How can one ever get diarrhea on C-rations? Aside from the first day, when sheer agony forced us to eat Chinese soup, we lived on C-rations for many, many months. Pete, whose job it was to supervise the cooking done by Ojisan's wife, was a man with a magnificently large imagination. Without any chef's training whatsoever, Peter was able to concoct a master-piece for each meal. The only complaint was it was always the same damn masterpiece.

C-rations come in varied cans, not in the multi-colored attractive cans of the American super-market but dull, green, grey cans that make you feel bilious just to look at them. The food consists of can one, beans and meat; can two, beef stew; can three, pork sausage without gravy; can four, beef and peas; can five, chicken and noodles. Peter would alternate these and mix the food with locally cooked rice, skilfully blending into this glorious mess just the right amount of B-1. What is B-1? This is another C-ration nightmare consisting of crackers, cocoa and jam. So that we could have breaded rice and meat, Peter cooked this *mélange*. Port Arthur, Texas' gift to Doctor Dooley was Peter Sherrer Kessey and his culi-nary masterpieces.

It was easy enough to joke about our food and extremely important that we do so. The maniacal monotony of our diet and the constant problems of digestion became terrible things. It is strange how large and overwhelming such small things as this can become when you're living in a jungle on the edge of the world. In order to maintain our mental equilibrium, it was important to keep high our sense of humor.

As the weeks progressed we became more renowned throughout the area. We always urged the villagers to pay us in barter for our medicines and for the treatment that we were giving. This was important for their own pride and was important for us too. It was expensive running this mission and I had made all my plans for Northern Laos and had brought most of my equipment prepared for cool or cold weather. As a consequence of not being allowed to go to the North, I had to buy a lot of different equipment. I was con-stantly worried that my money would run out before I ever would get to my destination, the North of Laos. Any saving of money became important to us and the simple idea of having our patients pay us in produce assumed great importance. At the end of a day in the clinic we would have a dozen eggs, several coconuts, perhaps a bottle of the local whiskey and, if the day was good, a scrawny chicken.

Every morning we would hold sick-call at our hospital. Then after lunch we would load the jeep up with medicines and hold a "jeep-call" in the afternoon. A jeep-call consisted of two members of the team driving to one of the dozens of outlying villages around Vang Vieng. The jeep would be driven into the village with the horn blaring. We would park, drop the tailgate, send someone for a bucket of water, and open the boxes of medicines. At once our portable clinic would be plunged into its flourishing practice. The people we would care for in the afternoons were those who were either too sick or not sick enough to make it to Vang Vieng, perhaps a four-hour walk away.

On jeep-call there was not the nerve-wracking pressure of misery and confinement that we felt in the crowded room at the clinic. At least we had mobility and a measure of fresh air. We knew the importance of going into the huts of these people. Never had they seen an American. Never had they received white men in their homes, and they were just as proud of their homes as we are. I would estimate that we have been in over three thousand Asian homes. Often the insides of these huts were oppressively sultry and humid. Most of them by our standards were filthy, and they were plagued with lice, fleas, gnats and insects. Always in the darkest corners there were the pot-bellied children, the under-nourished, the malnourished, and the miserable.

We always carried a black bag, a must for M.D.'s in America and a good idea in Laos, too. In the jeep we would bring extra boxes of combiotic, terramycin, Meals for Millions, sterile solutions, T-shirts and perhaps some candy as distractions and bribes for the young and old. A stateside friend sent me a boxful of small American flags. We had one huge flag flying over our house and others tacked to medical bags, kits and boxes. Denny rigged a fine little symbol of our country's splendor on the fender of our jeep. It was frequently torn by the brambles along the jungle trail and splattered by mud, but it nevertheless served proudly as our symbol of home.

We did not bleat about the glories of stateside plumbing; we spoke not at all of the beauties of Mount Vernon; we offered no praise for the democratic system; we did not proselytize. There were just two things that we identified ourselves by. The first was the American flag. And the second was the words with which we instructed our interpreters to precede every statement: *"Thanh mo America pun va* . . . The American doctor says." We wanted eloquence in deeds, not words.

In late winter I received a letter that made me feel like a village priest elevated to the Cardinalate. It informed me that the Junior Chamber of Commerce of the United States had voted me as one of their ten outstanding young men of 1956. This brought many blessings. One of them was that I was asked to become an honorary member of the Jaycees of Laos. This outfit was in its formative stage and was composed of leading young men of the capital. I joined and, at the only meeting I was ever able to attend, the Jaycees asked what they could do to help my mission. I had come here to help the Lao and the Lao in turn were offering their help to me.

Every couple of weeks two members of my team would take the drive through the jungle to get to Vientiane. They would pick up the mail, send ours out, buy whatever supplies were needed, load all into the trailer and return the next day to Vang Vieng. Every month we would have to buy another barrel of gasoline and gingerly carry it to our village on the tired back of Agnes.

Though it was always a break to get away from the clinic, the jeep drive was a frightening experience. If the vehicle should break down, it was certain that the two men would have to have a hike of several days in order to get to the capital. There was rarely any traffic on the road during these months. In spite of Baker's administerings, Agnes was limping and lugging herself around, showing the result of her arduous and frequent jeep-calls.

Once in Vientiane, our spirits would climb. Buoyancy and humor are requirements for men in my kind of work. To us the best part of Vientiane was the house of Howard and Martha Kaufman. Howard was certainly the best friend we had in the kingdom. He is an anthropologist and, to my knowledge, the only government-employed American in the kingdom who has taken time out to learn to speak the native Lao. He is with Community Development Programs of the United States Operations Mission but unfortunately due to "the exigencies of a large mission" he is not given opportunity to leave the capital to get to the communities. His wife Martha, though only about twenty-five years old, was almost a mother to us all. Martha never batted an eye when we would arrive filthy from a many-hour drive, timing our entry with their dinner hour. Water would be ready and we would have a hot shower and clean up. We always kept some fresh clothes in Howard's dresser. Martha would have more food prepared and we would sit around a table (instead of a crate) and sit on chairs (instead of the floor) and eat a dinner (instead of C-ration).

Months later, when my University of Notre Dame men joined us and we frequently said the family rosary aloud at night, I heard Protestant Pete Kessey complaining to Howard about it: "Seems you can hardly get to sleep at night, up there in the jungle, what with the Catholics clicking their beads all the time."

I cannot give full praise to these three men of mine and the two who later joined us. These men did the dirty work, seldom grumbling and usually joking a bit. They were excellent men in every sense of the word. Peter Kessey had a willing heart and a gentle hand; he spoke to the people in a Texas-American accent, and somehow they always seemed to understand. Norman Baker, my French-speaking mechanic and general man around the place, could slap on a dressing that was guaranteed never to come off; he would sweat and grunt but he got it on and it stayed on. Denny Shepard, who was going on to medical school, was brilliant and practiced a high caliber of medicine. I am afraid Dooley was a hard taskmaster; I frequently lost my temper, but the boys persisted. I believe that my men showed heroism, sacrifice and guts, not in any one great dramatic action, but rather in constancy.

4

"Phasing Out;" The Ceremony of *Baci*

We kept a $20 bill tacked upon the wall. The understanding was that anyone who got mad, or homesick, or just fed up with the job could take it and head for home. No one ever touched that money. But I am sure there were many times that the boys were tempted during those endless days and nights of dealing with misery, filth and disease.

Denny, the newlywed, missed his wife terribly, and spent his odd moments composing lengthy letters. Norman Baker became increasingly jittery as the time for the baby's arrival drew near. (Fortunately, my mother kept in close touch with Priscilla; and when Master Arthur Thomas Baker showed up one day in November, the excited father got the good news in less than 72 hours, thanks to the Embassy mail-room in Vientiane!)

All of us developed a sort of compulsive fear of contamination. We were always conscious of the contagiousness of everything we touched. No matter how many times we scrubbed up during the day, washing our hands in alcohol until the skin became dry and brittle, we felt a mad desire toward evening to burn our clothes and literally bathe in alcohol.

Instead, someone would yell: *"Ab nam Nam Song!"* ("Let's head for the river!") We'd shuck our clothes on the embankment, plunge in, and spend the next half-hour soaping ourselves. Still, we never felt entirely clean.

That was what gave Pete the idea for the shower. To start with he had only a shower-head which he had swiped from the hotel in Vientiane. But he dreamed up a weird arrangement which involved a 55-gallon gasoline drum rigged on a tripod about 18 feet high. With the help of Ojisan and a few coolies he set out in search of lumber. The only hardwood available was teak—it took four strong men to lift one five-foot beam. That never fazed Pete.

After two weeks and much sweating and swearing the shower was finished. It looked like a cross between a Texas

46

oil derrick and the Leaning Tower of Pisa. The big barrel was lowered on a block and tackle, and filled with water. Then the line was hitched to Agnes. The jeep drove down the road and raised the 400-pound load. When the barrel was secure in its supporting cradle, someone would climb the rig and light the little kerosene lamp on a shelf beneath it.

It took about two hours to heat the 55 gallons of water to ideal temperature. The whole operation was fantastic; but everyone who scrubbed himself under that steaming water agreed that *la douche de Pierre* (Pete's Shower) was a huge success. At least we all felt a bit cleaner.

One day in November we were busy as usual, and at midday we just bolted our food and went back to work. While nobody mentioned it, we were all aware that the day was Thanksgiving. We were just a little more homesick than usual. Then, along toward dusk, we heard the roar of a jeep. A cloud of dust boiled up the road to our house and out stepped a short, chubby young man with a wonderful smile—Jefferson Davis Cheek of Comanche, Texas.

Jeff Cheek, who was attached to the USOM in Vientiane, was one of our few and infrequent visitors. Now he announced that he was dirty, tired and hungry after the long trek from Vientiane. He demanded to know what we had to eat.

"C-rations brother!" said Pete. "Today it's beef and peas plus rice." Jeff laughed and hauled a dusty bag out of the back of his jeep. It contained a complete Thanksgiving dinner —roast turkey, cranberry sauce, mashed potatoes, pumpkin pie. He had even brought along the alcoholic trimmings, which we enjoyed while the food was heating in the hospital sterilizer.

After we had feasted royally, we sat out on the porch and talked about Savong, the little girl Jeff once had brought to us from Ban Tsieng.

We had been in Vang Vieng only a few weeks when Jeff Cheek came to visit us for the first time. He was driving along the jungle trail, when a group of natives stopped his jeep and appealed for help. They showed him a little girl, about 14 years old, lying on a mat, semi-conscious and obviously near death.

This was Savong. Some time earlier, no one knew how long ago, she had scratched her leg in the jungle and it became infected. Ignorant and helpless, Savong's people just left her lying in the hut. Eventually, the entire leg became horribly bloated and the infection spread up into the groin. That was the way Jeff found her.

He placed her gently in the back of the jeep, and drove slowly through the jungle, reaching Vang Vieng after dark. We opened up the hospital, but after one look I had my doubts about saving her. Yet there was something about this child that touched us deeply. She seemed symbolic of all the miserable, neglected kids in Laos—Southeast Asia is full of Savongs. So we were determined to save her.

Of course, she was filthy after such long neglect. We literally had to scrub the nearly lifeless little body with soap and brush before proceeding. Then, when she was clean, we gave her a minimum of anesthesia, and I began to operate.

I had to incise the bloated leg from knee to groin. The horrible green pus filled several containers. When the drainage stopped, I saw the cellulitis, which can best be described as a mass of boils involving the muscles and underlying tissues. When we got through, there was nothing left of that massive leg but bone and a few soggy muscles.

She had lain for so many months in one position, that her "good" side was covered with massive, weeping pressure sores which we cleaned and dressed. Then we revived her and administered infusions of saline and glucose.

Pete, Denny, Baker and even Chai took turns hovering over Savong all through that night and the next day. The fever dropped, she brightened, and then began to cry. Not from pain now, but because her anguish was over. Between sobs we heard her mumbling "Cop chai, cop chai, cop chai. . . ." Over and over—"Thank you, thank you, thank you. . . ."

Weeks passed and Savong grew stronger. First she sat up, then she walked a few steps. The boys trimmed her hair in a sort of feather-bob, gave her a toothbrush and taught her how to use it. Somehow they even obtained female clothes. Then Jeff Cheek came with presents of hair-ribbons and combs. We decided that Savong really looked beautiful.

Months later we discharged her. She was strong and well, although she limped a bit on that frail little leg. Her people came to take her back to Ban Tsieng.

Before she left we took a picture of her. We gave one print to Jeff Cheek because, we said teasingly, Savong was "his girl." The other print we kept for ourselves. Whenever we felt homesick or disheartened we would look at that picture of Savong. It served to remind us that, for some people, things might have been different had we stayed comfortably at home.

Toward dusk one evening, early in December, I watched the crowd gather in front of our house for movies. Peter and Denny hung the screen from our front porch. Baker, timing his entrance like a professional, picked up the 130-pound generator and carried it through the crowd to its place near the projector—his strongman act was an unfailing hit at every performance.

When the picture began I took my favorite seat on the porch, above and behind the screen. From there I could study these wonderful faces, young and old, glowing in the light reflected from the screen, captivated by the colorful magic of Walt Disney's *Fantasia*. I remembered how we had once considered dubbing in a Lao sound-track on these movies, and then abandoned the scheme as too costly. Now I was glad we had left them as they were. Walt Disney's creations have a universal language of their own.

I thought: How many times had I been told that the Lao were lazy people, ignorant, backward, indifferent to their own betterment? How many times has that canard been uttered by cynical westerners against neglected people everywhere who never had a chance? Here in Vang Vieng I had living proof of its falsity. Never have I seen people respond so readily to encouragement, or to make so much from so little help.

Our classes in sanitation, hygiene, food and nutrition, infant and child care were popular and paying off handsomely. We had "bagged" many midwives, and these girls had achieved an *esprit de corps* that had elevated midwifery to a proud profession that attracted other candidates. The Lao nurses were increasing in number and proficiency. Each fortnight, by arrangement, when the boys made the trip to Vientiane for mail and supplies, they brought back a senior from the *lycée* for a week. We hoped to inspire these young men to study medicine. Already we had trained a dozen "practical" nurses, more than were needed in Vang Vieng.

Now, I knew, the time was approaching when we would have to "phase out" of Vang Vieng. My mission was not to set up a permanent American outpost, but to establish something that the Lao themselves could carry on. True, it would be primitive by western standards; but it would be better than what these people had before.

I believe that those of us who attempt to aid in a foreign land must be content with small achievements. Americans in the capital said that I practiced 19th-century medicine. They are correct, I did practice 19th-century medicine, and this was just fine. Upon my departure our indigenous personnel would practice 18th-century medicine. Good, this is progress, since most of the villagers live in the 15th century.

So that phase of the plan was settled in my own mind. Kam Lak, the senior nurse, would take charge. He was a conscientious, highly intelligent young man who already could be entrusted with minor surgery. Kam Ba, his wife, who was probably the best of our midwives, could serve as his assistant. We left them a few surgical instruments and about $10,000 worth of drugs. The Ministry promised them further supplies.

My boys were scheduled to depart for home within the next month or so. Baker was anxious to get back to his wife and baby; Denny Shepard, who also had a bride waiting, had to get back to the university, as did Pete Kessey. I had two replacements lined up; I was just waiting for one more letter from South Bend, Indiana, which would clinch the deal. Then. . . .

The movies ended, and the crowd began to drift away. The boys took down the movie screen, stowed the gear, and began to bat around our living room before turning in.

"Gentlemen," I said, "I have news for you." Baker groaned loudly, and rolled over on the cot. (He claimed that whenever I addressed them that way another dirty job was coming up.) "For a job well done you get shore leave from—I hope—December 22nd, reporting back to Vientiane on January 2nd, 1957. Expenses paid—within reason. I would suggest you spend the holidays in Hong Kong."

Of course, they were jubilant. But I felt this was a small reward for all they had done. When they worked for me, they had no Saturdays or Sundays off. Denny wanted to know where I would be.

"I'm going to Manila," I said. "But I'll be back in Vientiane the day after New Year's. It's time for me to see the high brass. I've got to know what the score is."

I spent the holidays in Manila where I delivered some lectures. Then, on January 2nd, I arrived in Vientiane and went directly to see Dr. Oudom at the Ministry of Health. He greeted me enthusiastically, and told me that the Premier wished to see me. This was quite a surprise, but Dr. Oudom smilingly refused to elaborate. We went over to the Ministry where, after a short wait, we were ushered into the Premier's office.

Prince SouvannaPhouma spoke glowingly of my mission in Vang Vieng. Much to my amazement, he seemed to be familiar with every detail of our operations, the nurse and midwife training programs, the hygiene and sanitation classes, the jeep-call system, etc. Then he inquired about my plans for the future.

When I explained that my funds were running low, and that I could remain in Laos only about four months more, it was his turn to register surprise. Apparently, he hadn't fully realized that Dooley, and not rich old Uncle Sam, was footing the bills!

It was then that he made his magnanimous offer. Beginning immediately, he said, the Royal Lao Government would provide *toutes les facilités*. The army would furnish transportation and supplies. The Ministry of Education would furnish anything I needed for an educational program. I would have free access to the government's medical supplies. The government would even pay the salaries of my Lao personnel.

This was almost too good to be true. But I decided I might as well shoot for the moon—*Bau pinh yanh!*

"Your Excellency," I said, "don't you think my medical mission could accomplish more for the Royal Government if you sent me into one of the northern provinces?"

"I most certainly do!" he said emphatically. I looked over and saw Dr. Oudoam's beaming smile.

The Premier then mentioned two possible areas of operation, Muong Sing, a town near the Burma border, and—Nam Tha! He explained that both villages now had operational landing strips. He would put a small plane at my disposal and he would keep a supply line open. Of course, there were still certain dangers in the north, he added. But there were police and soldiers from the local garrison who would be assigned to me as bodyguards.

I thanked him sincerely. Aglow with the good news, I went to the American Embassy, and asked to see Ambassador Parsons. Again, I had a pleasant surprise. This time the Ambassador greeted me warmly, and congratulated me for the fine job we were doing in Vang Vieng. When I told him about my conversation with the Premier, he seemed delighted.

"Yes, Dr. Dooley," he said, "I really think it would be a splendid idea for you to go north now."

Ambassador Parsons explained that conditions in Laos were much more stable now. Border incidents were less likely. With the opening of the airstrip at Nam Tha, closer and speedier contact was now possible. Moreover, he said, our work in Vang Vieng had won the confidence and respect of the Lao Government. We were less likely to be taken for spies or *agents provocateurs*.

Now I faced the difficult task of "closing out" of Vang Vieng. Fortunately, I still had my three veterans, Baker, Pete and Denny, to help me. I met them at the Samboun Hotel, and they heard the good news with mixed feelings.

Baker already had booked his passage on a flight leaving in mid-January. Denny Shepard decided to go up to Nam Tha and spend a few weeks helping me get settled. Pete Kessey, the lone bachelor of the trio, scratched his head thoughtfully. He was due back in Austin for the Spring term of pharmacy school. "Well, shucks," he said, "they can get along without me, Doc. Guess I'll string along with you for a few months more."

We piled our bags in the jeep, and for the last time Agnes made the rugged trip through the jungle to Vang Vieng. Poor Agnes! She wouldn't be going north with us. The Premier and Dr. Oudom had warned me that there were no roads in Nam Tha.

In Vang Vieng we told Chai and Si that we were leaving for the North soon and of course we wanted them to come with us. They just uttered a low moan. But when we said that they could quit if they were fearful of the North, they looked insulted and said, "Where you go, we will come always."

Ojisan was unhappy to see us leave as we had become good friends. We assured him that Vang Vieng would always be our first love but that the people of Vang Vieng had taught us many things. One of the things they had taught us was the care and responsibility of our neighbors. Ojisan himself had so frequently pointed out the importance of driving to the surrounding villages for jeep-calls. Now we were going to do the same thing, but we were just going very far away. We also told him that we hoped the United States Operations Mission would come to Vang Vieng with some programs, either in education or perhaps even in medicine or agriculture. Ojisan hoped they would, too. Later, they did.

We held our last class in the local school and asked the children to remember what we had taught them. They replied that they would not forget their Americans. We graduated and "bagged" some more girls from the midwife training course and began to plan out days in January.

We were timing this phase out. We did not wish to offend the village by leaving abruptly so we planned to spend four or five weeks doing our work as usual, explaining to each day's sick-call that we would soon be leaving and that the Lao nurse and midwives would continue our work. We told all the villages that these people were very capable and that we would leave the white man's miraculous medicines behind for the villagers. They were sad to see us go but pleased that we were leaving things behind.

The town of Vang Vieng gave us an elaborate *baci,* a ritualistic ceremony, climaxed by a grand feast, which the Lao hold to celebrate a birth, a marriage, a soldier's return from the wars, or the departure of cherished friends. The women of the village built a small pyramid from palm leaves, and decorated it with flowers, candles, baubles, and bangles. The finished product stood about two feet high. It was then placed in a beautiful hand-made silver bowl. From the top of the pyramid to the bottom of the bowl long streamers of white cotton were hung. Around the base of the bowl the women placed, with great precision, succulent pieces of pork, rice, sweetmeats and other delicacies.

All the participants in the *baci* then sat in a large circle on new mats or blankets around the center pyramid of flowers, close enough to lean forward and touch the bowl with an outstretched hand.

An old sorcerer then chanted the Invocation to the Spirits. We sat on the floor with our long legs tucked beside us, our left hand held up as if in prayer, and our right palm extended upwards touching the bowl. In his chant, the sorcerer asked Sakke, who lives in the Paradise of Sixteen Floors, to come join us. He called on Kame, who lives in Kamaphob; and on Charoupe, who lives in the Divine Spheres. He begged Khirisi, who dwells in the mountains and the rivers to come with Attarikhe, who abounds in Sweet Air. He begged all the divinities of Dawn and Dusk, the spirits of Night and Day, and the nymphs of the Mountains and Flowers to come to this *baci* and partake of the food which is laid out for them.

After the sorcerer felt that all the spirits were present, he called on the souls of those for whom the *baci* was being given. The Lao tribes feel that the soul is a vagabond, and must be recalled to the body from time to time. In a sing-song fashion he incanted words which meant "Come, be with us, Souls, return to your home of flesh, fear not the tiger nor the phantoms, come to us here now where the good divinities and spirits have come; fear not, return to your bodies. . . ." According to the Lao belief, there are thirty-two parts of the human body and each possesses a soul. So the sorcerer had to implore each of the thirty-two parts; this took a little time. When both the spirits and the souls had finally arrived, we sat back and rested a moment. The second part of the *baci* then began.

The sorcerer first took a piece of cotton string from the center pyramid of blossoms and knelt in front of those for whom the *baci* was being offered. He made a wish for me, and while chanting his wish he tied a string around my wrist, and very meticulously twirled the ends lest the wish fall out of the string. When he finished with me, a second person tied another cotton on my wrist, and a third and so on. This was repeated for each of us. By the time the ceremony was finished, we had more than a dozen cotton strings around our wrists. Each offered a wish, and each was a bit more bizarre than the former:

"May you always be strong against the tusks of elephants."

"May you be safe from the jaws of the wild boar."

"May you be rich."

"May you have many wives."

"May you possess all wisdom and health."

"May you be blessed with prosperity and strength."

"May your jeep not fall off the road nor your airplane from the sky."

"May you always carry with you our love."

"May you return to us, your friends."

The old betel-chewing women, the wise elders of the village, the giggling girls, the mayor, all tied on us the cotton strings of friendship and called on the presiding spirits to witness the sincerity of their wishes.

Chai had told us that the person receiving the *baci*, to show his gratitude and understanding, must do his part. So after each string was tied, we clasped our hands together in praying attitude and said, *"Cop chai liiiiii, saaaa."*

After the *baci* was finished, the sorcerer again thanked the spirits and told them they might leave, and the souls that they might return to their life of roaming. Then everyone started to eat the rice balls, sweatmeats and the other food that the spirits didn't eat. And of course we drank lots of *choum,* the local rice alcohol.

Finally the day came for our leaving. We had everything crated up and were sitting on the front porch of our now-empty house. The army trucks that the Minister was sending up to us were due in an hour.

Hundreds of people had gathered in the square to bid us farewell. We had *baci* strings tied around our wrists almost up to the elbow. The villagers brought many going-away gifts—flowers, corn, chicken, the local whiskey; gifts of good wishes. We said many farewells to Ojisan, the nurse, the mayor, the kids. We were all sitting around feeling melancholy; but soon the trucks would be here and our melancholy would dissolve in the sweat of loading.

We waited all morning, all afternoon. We unrolled our sleeping bags and slept all night. Next day the trucks arrived. The army drivers had no explanation whatever nor did we demand any. We were used to this sort of thing and did not let it bother us any more. Again there were many farewells, more flowers, more corn, more gifts. We even felt bad saying goodbye to the betel-chewing oldsters. They had become our friends.

The last glimpse we had of the villagers of Vang Vieng was from the back of an army truck as it jolted along toward the jungle road. They looked like a lot of little bears, pawing the air as they waved their arms *toward themselves* in the parting gesture that means "come back soon."

5

Nam Tha at Last

When we arrived in Vientiane, there was the inevitable foul-up. The airline had advanced the departure of Baker's flight by one hour without bothering to give us more than 15 minutes notice. We barely made it. Cussing air travel like a true sailor, Baker managed to dash through customs and heave his own bags aboard the plane just before the door closed. As the plane took off, I suddenly realized that my friend and assistant, Norman Baker had left before I could adequately thank him for his work and his kindly fellowship.

Denny took charge of preparations for the move to Nam Tha, while Pete Kessey and I made the two-hour flight to Bangkok to meet our two new men. On the way, I told Pete what little I knew about these boys.

Among the scores of letters I had received from volunteers, there was one from John deVitry, an undergraduate at Notre Dame, my alma mater. He was the son of French parents, now American citizens; and his reasons for wanting to serve a stretch with us in Laos impressed me. I wrote to my old friend, Miss Erma Konya, who is on the administrative staff of the University, and asked her to investigate him. Her report on John deVitry was highly favorable, and she recommended another boy, Robert E. Waters. We corresponded, and the deal was settled.

We saw them off the plane at the Bangkok airport, two typical crew-cut college boys, somewhat bedraggled after the 45-hour flight. Pete Kessey groaned: "O Lord, Joe College and his roommate. I'll bet they even brought their hi-fi gear and recording albums with them!"

John deVitry was a tall, slender, sensitive and serious-minded fellow, 21 years old. Bob Waters was only 20, but tall, well built, and obviously the extrovert type. They both looked pretty soft and green for the part of the world where we would be operating.

If I shared Pete's original misgivings, I am happy to report that we were both dead wrong. "Joe College" is a common masquerade; beneath those campus-cut clothes lie the heart and

sinews of our nation. Both boys turned out to be prodigious
workers. John was a born diplomat, something the Dooley
mission needed badly. Within thirty days they were both
crusty and uncomplaining veterans taking life on the China
border in their stride. I guess we all have to start somewhere.

Now that the rainy season was finished, and a landing strip
ready for us at Nam Tha, we prepared to go north. Denny
had purchased all the things on the list, and we brought many
new supplies from Bangkok, plus two new men. We were
to fly in two trips. The first one would be a Bristol airplane,
the second a DC-3. Before loading we estimated our weight on
paper and divided the gear accordingly. When the trucks got
to the airport we were able to weigh the boxes exactly. To
Pete's horror we found that it would be impossible to transport all the lumber. He had meticulously dissected the Vang
Vieng shower and brought it along with hopes of reconstructing it in Nam Tha. We loaded the aircraft and with a feeling
of poignancy left *la douche de Pierre* behind us.

We left Vientiane in a huge, obsolete Bristol cargo plane
with a belly like a landing craft, tremendous wings, and a
pair of undersized propellers. For the next three hours we
flew north over a cloud layer pierced occasionally by jagged
mountain peaks. Then we descended and saw the vast rain-
forest of the Nam Tha valley. It looked like a rich green
carpet decorated with the scarlet of flame-trees and the soft
blossoms of frangipani.

The rain-forest trees are devoured by clinging, tenacious
tendrils and trailers, saprophytes, clawing into the fleshy bark
trying to consume the very core of the tree. One might draw
a corollary with the techniques of Communist conquest in
Asia.

The French pilot made several passes at the little landing
strip. Then we began to climb again, and the co-pilot came
back and said, *"Trop petite!"* The muddy strip was too short
for the cumbersome, overloaded Bristol. I went up to the
cockpit and persuaded the pilot to try again. He looked at me
pityingly, and shrugged with Gallic indifference. We swooped
in and skidded to a stop with only a few feet of the runway
to spare.

When we opened the doors of the plane, we found a large
crowd of villagers gathered around. We jumped down to the
ground and knew that at last we were on the soil of the north.
Two years ago, straight east of here, we had worked in North

Viet Nam. For years I had dreamed of working here. For a year I had planned it, and for the past five months we had been proving ourselves and our mission. And now we had arrived. We were in the northernmost fingertip of freedom jammed into the underbelly of Communist China. This was a dramatic moment for us all. None of us said very much. We knew that halfway up that first range of hills just north of us was the rim of hell.

Despite its isolation, Nam Tha proved to be a bigger and more progressive village than Vang Vieng. We traveled afoot from the airstrip into town. Our tons of supplies and equipment had to be moved by sheer coolie-power. The trail led directly into the apex of the triangular area which is Nam Tha's public "square," lined with houses and shops, an elaborate Buddhist temple, the police headquarters and local jail, and the "mansion" of the Chao Khuong, or Governor of the province.

Halfway along the base of the triangle we found the house that we were to occupy. It was a solidly constructed building formerly occupied by the Chao Khuong itself. In one part was a telegraph office and the living quarters of Pavie, the operator, and his large family. Another room was occupied by a couple of young school teachers. We asked everyone to stay put. Chai, Si, our houseboy, and Kieu, our new interpreter (who spoke English and once had worked for the American Embassy), took the room near the school teachers. Bob, John, Denny and I took over two large rooms. Pete Kessey, yearning for privacy, found a small, dark closet which he named "The Black Hole" and converted it into a bedroom. We did not close any part of the house off; doors were always open and Pavie, the teachers, and just about anyone who wished to could meander in and out of our living room. Their naked babies were just as much at home in our part of the house as in any other part.

Only a short walk from the house we found the recently completed (on the Premier's orders) dispensary building. We went to work on the hospital as soon as we could. The main dispensary building was transformed to the main hospital building. It did not take too much to do this. The building was about thirty-five feet long, divided into three rooms. We left one room entirely in the hands of the Lao dispensary nurses, changed the second one to be used as an office, and the third one became the Sick-Call Room.

We built a large table, covered it with linoleum, and placed it in the Sick-Call Room. At the house we had a small generator that we used for the movie projector. In Vientiane we had purchased a very bright desk lamp, and hooked this to the operating room table and onto the generator. Now we had an operating room.

We kept the small pressure sterilizer in our house, and carried the sterile goods back and forth on our bicycles. The hospital compound was about a five-minute ride from the house. The generator was slung under a pole when it had to be transported, or from time to time we could use the Chao Khuong's jeep.

An abandoned bamboo building next to the Clinic was cleaned up and painted. We had to wait several weeks until they found enough lime in the mountains. When mixed with water this made a pretty good whitewash. John, Bob and the coolies built fifteen beds from teak wood and old army metal cots. We spent several days cutting out pictures from the old magazines that we had, and pasted these to the walls to brighten up the place. When the ward was finished it looked fine, by anyone's standards.

A third building was fixed up as a sort of "isolation ward" for leprosy cases. This was not up on stilts like the ward, but was a small thatched hut. We built nine bamboo cots here. Thus it did not take long to have a three-building hospital in good shape.

True to his word, the Premier had prepared the way for us. The Chao Khuong and the local representative of the Ministry of Public Works did everything possible to help us. Nguyen Cauvin, the public works official, was an amusing and pathetic character, half French, half Vietnamese. He had done a good job on the schools and had built our hospital. But his great ambition was to build a road across the province from Nam Tha to the Burma border. Lacking modern road-building equipment, and depending solely on the hand labor of coolies, he had never been able to progress farther than the muddy trail that ran about 10 miles past the airstrip and was washed away each year during the monsoon season. Cauvin became one of our best friends.

The Chao Khuong was a curious but likable fellow. He spoke rapid-fire French, but always through a cloud of cigarette smoke, and without ever removing the butt from his lips except to light another. Only John, our diplomat, could completely understand him, so they became bosom pals.

The first time I asked the Governor to dine with us, he accepted with a grave bow—and never showed up. When we went after him, he explained that he had not received the proper invitation in writing, as was customary in France. I explained that, in America, a verbal invitation was considered correct for informal occasions. He nodded smilingly, and seemed satisfied. However, when we invited him after that he would always raise his eyebrows and inquire: "—à la français, ou à l'américaine?"

Denny Shepard decided to devote the short time he would be with us in Nam Tha to setting up a clean, efficient, adequately stocked surgery. So he went right to work installing equipment and sterilizing instruments, and making our sterile packs and surgical drapes. It was a good thing he did. For surgery started sooner than we expected.

On our second day in Nam Tha we heard a great commotion in the village. Escorted by the Chao Khuong himself, some natives appeared at the compound carrying two "sedan chairs" crudely fashioned from bamboo and slung on long poles. I went out and took a look at the occupants, and yelled to the boys to get the operating room ready for an emergency.

But this was more than an emergency. It was our first evidence of Communist "banditry" on the northern frontier. While Denny and I scrubbed up, the Chao Khuong told us the story. Apparently the bandits had swooped down on this Yao tribesman's hut in a little village near the border. They had hacked at the occupants with long swords, literally quartering the grandmother and a small child, and critically wounding the tribesman and his wife. The carnage did not last long. When neighbors, attracted by the screams, reached the hut the bandits had fled—stealing nothing.

The villagers placed the wounded couple in the improvised sling-chairs and made the arduous journey down the valley to Nam Tha. It had taken a day and a night, and how the victims survived the ordeal I will never know.

The woman's head, face, and breasts were severely slashed, and the wounds were already infected. She had a raging fever, and was in excruciating pain. We gave her antibiotics and morphine, and turned our attention to the husband, who was in worse shape.

Half his scalp had been neatly lifted from the skull, apparently by one sweep of a sharp knife or sword. His jawbone was broken in several places, and one side of his face was slashed away from the eyelid down to the lips. He had a fractured arm and a lot of gashes.

Cleaning and suturing the scalp was comparatively simple. The maddening task was repairing the multiple fractures of the jaw. Because all the teeth had been knocked out, there was no way to hold all the fractured ends in approximation, so I had to remove a large section of the broken jaw and part of the dental structure. Then I sutured the gum, and repaired the face, lip and eyelid, and went to work on the fractured arm.

With the help of antibiotics, anti-tetanus shots, and a lot of intravenous feeding, the unfortunate fellow eventually pulled through. But he will never be a pretty sight.

The woman's head was such a mass of infections that nothing could be sutured immediately. I was able to repair the face and the mutilated breasts without too much trouble. Our main job was to keep her alive, clear up the infections, and finish the surgical work later.

The Chao Khuong and one of his officers had remained in the operating room during the entire bloody procedure. When it was over the Governor wandered outside and lit the inevitable cigarette. After I had washed up, and wandered outside, he was still there, puffing away pensively.

"That's the way it goes," he said sadly. "We'll send out a patrol, and find—nothing. For a while that village can sleep in peace. Next time the devils will strike elsewhere."

There were a lot of questions I hesitated to ask him. Who were these border bandits? Did they come from Red China? Or did they belong to the Pathet Lao? But I had been warned in Vientiane not to pry deeply into such matters. And, on such short acquaintance, I knew I had to watch my step with the Chao Khuong. The Governor pointed out that this beating was just another indication that "peace" did not exist in this part of Asia, even though this was the year of a million blossoms. The hideousness of Communism is much in evidence here. Ambassador Parsons was justified in his fears for us and our work in this area.

The Chao Khuong invited me to visit his residence the following evening for a good talk. Unfortunately, I had to break that engagement. For the next night we were busy with another "basket case" which taught us that we had to cope with a different kind of enemy: witch doctors.

6

The Story of Ion; Witch Doctors

Along toward nightfall a man came to our house begging us to save his 10-year-old son who lay near death in the mountain village of Ban Pareng. What was wrong? The boy had been burned, the man said, "black like a chicken or pig." When had this happened? The man stopped to calculate time.

"Fourteen nights ago," he said. "The night was very cold. Ion, my son, wore three extra shirts to keep warm. He backed closer and closer to the fire. Then his shirts burst into flame."

The soldier from the constabulary who brought the man to us urged us to wait until morning. The trail to Ban Pareng, he said, was treacherous. Besides, if the boy had lived for fourteen nights and days, he would probably keep until to-morrow. (*Bau pinh yanh!*)

But the father was frantic; the case sounded both serious and puzzling, and, besides, we would be busy with sick-call in the morning. Pete, Denny, and Chai found flashlights, and I checked the contents of my bag. Then we told the man to lead the way. We took the road leading out beyond the air-strip—Cauvin's "road." Now we learned why jeep-calls were impossible in Nam Tha.

Walking in single file, we made our way through the jungle. Then we found the mountain trail and started to climb. For the next hour or more we clambered up steep rocks, and crossed several rope-and-bamboo bridges that swayed peril-ously over torrential rivers. An old man of 30, I was ex-hausted when we reached the little village of Ban Pareng.

We were ushered into a large, gloomy hut, perched high on stilts. The room reeked with the acrid odor of burnt flesh. The father led us to what looked like a pile of filthy rags lying in one corner. In the flashlight beam I saw a wisp of a boy sprawled on his stomach.

The lad was charred black from shoulders to buttocks. He was barely conscious, and lay motionless in the most dis-torted posture. Yet the boy's entire back seemed alive with motion. I pushed the light closer. The back was swarming with maggots feasting on the charred flesh.

The father explained that after the accident the local witch doctor had smeared the burns with a paste which I later learned was compounded of pig grease, betel-nut juice, and cow-dung. The deep third-degree burns were bad enough. But this grotesque treatment, probably repeated several times over the fortnight, had helped to produce this horrible living death.

There was nothing we could do under the circumstances. If the boy remained in the hut much longer he would certainly be dead. Getting him down the mountain and into Nam Tha seemed almost impossible, but it was our only chance. We told the father to find a large basket, some rope and a strong pole. Pete and Chai remained behind to supervise the perilous "ambulance" operation. Denny and I found a guide and started back to Nam Tha.

We were scrubbed up and ready when our basket case arrived at the hospital some hours later. We put Ion on the table, sprawled on his belly, and Pete took over the tricky job of administering the open-drip anesthesia. Our generator had not yet been hooked up; and, because of the dangerous ether fumes, we couldn't light the oil lamps. Fortunately, we had several battery-powered "miner's lamps" that could be strapped on our heads. They served perfectly in this emergency.

We flooded the boy's back with soap and water, and gently scrubbed away the filth. I began to debride the dead tissue, and soon found myself down to the bones of the rib cage. It was much worse than I had anticipated. The muscles of the shoulder girdle had been severely damaged, and huge areas of the buttocks completely destroyed.

Finally, Ion was bundled in antiseptic ointment and fluff gauze, and gently carried to a bed. After weeks of neglect, with little food or water, the pathetic little body was weak and dehydrated. We tried to administer fluids intravenously, but we couldn't find a vein that hadn't collapsed. We even had difficulty finding muscles on the emaciated body that would take a penicillin injection.

Denny and Pete spent what was left of that night pushing fluids subcutaneously into Ion's abdomen and legs. At best, he was what could be described as an "extremely poor surgical risk." (By some miracle, he survived and got well, a terribly deformed little boy.)

We had seen some severe burns and injuries in Vang Vieng. I knew that we probably would see even worse cases in the isolated north. But how often, I wondered, would our troubles be compounded, as in Ion's case, by the weird practices of primitive "witch doctors"?

I was not sure that a child like this could live even in all the sterile magnificence of an American hospital. Here we were, half a world away, working with flashlights, a minimum of equipment, and on a case most doctors would declare futile. But the children of Laos seem weathered to hardship and pain, and Ion had the guts he needed. With the power of medicine, blended with the power of prayer, and sprinkled with a little sweat, Ion pulled through. When he awoke he found his bed brightly decorated with multi-colored balloons and he found his day-and-night corpsmen very happy. How much we have learned here in Asia. There is a oneness in this world.

After the operation I walked slowly back to our hut. My boys all voted to sit up the rest of the night with Ion. Seeing these young men devoting their most tired hours to that child seared something into me. It is the simple clear-cut realization that the brotherhood of man does exist, as surely as does the Fatherhood of God. Indeed, we are our brothers' keepers.

Before we came to Nam Tha, and perhaps from time immemorial, the witch doctors had ruled supreme. No one ever questioned their wisdom or the power of their nostrums or incantations. But now the wretched people were torn between the magic of the traditional sorcerers and the new ways of the white medicine-men.

Finally the witch doctors put a "hex" on our hospital. They surrounded the compound with little mats of woven bamboo mounted on short posts stuck in the ground. That may sound silly. But, for all practical purposes, that hex worked like the proverbial charm. No one, no matter how desperately ill, would come near our hospital for help.

These witch doctors were all respected village elders. But our two most formidable adversaries were Old Joe and a crone we called Maggie.

So we decided to adopt an old American stratagem—"if you can't lick 'em, join 'em." Instead of antagonizing the witch doctors (and this may raise the hackles of the American Medical Association), we began to treat them as "colleagues in the healing arts" who practiced a somewhat different discipline of medicine with which we disagreed and yet respected.

One afternoon I returned from an emergency call in the jungle to find Pete holding an earnest professional conference with Old Joe. Pete gave me the eye, and I squatted down and listened respectfully.

Old Joe had spread out before him a weird assortment of sticks, bamboo slivers, betel nuts, boiled leaves, pig grease, cow dung, and was explaining the theory behind his *materia medica*. Most of it was fantastic. But here and there I recognized fragments of the universal folk remedies (like the use of spiderwebs in open wounds), the effectiveness of which are acknowledged by modern medicine.

"Well," said Pete, "we just belong to different schools of medicine. We use different drugs, different methods, but we are both working for the same thing—to free the people from the evils of disease and suffering. The important thing is for us to work together. We'll teach you what we know, and you will teach us." That sounded fair enough to Old Joe.

From that time on Old Joe rarely missed a sick-call. We would administer a shot of penicillin, Joe would invoke the proper spirits. We would splint a fracture, then permit Old Joe to tie the indispensable red, white and black strings around the splints. If we were paid two coconuts for fee, Old Joe received one. (In America this practice is held in a bad light; they call it "fee splitting.")

His recovery rate had never been so high, so Old Joe was happy—and became our staunch friend. (However, he never acquired much faith in antibiotics. It was absurd, he said, to stick a needle in someone's backside when the infection was in the patient's head!)

Maggie was my own special problem, but whenever I held sick-call she rarely left my side. She was a snaggle-toothed old crone, and the dirtiest woman in the village, dressed in a ragged western-style blouse and skirt with a filthy towel wrapped around her head. Maggie shaved her head regularly, but she never washed her hands.

After handling each filthy patient, I would carefully wash my hands in soap and water, then hold them out while an assistant poured alcohol over them. Maggie was fascinated. I patiently explained that soap and water plus some of this powerful liquid banished any "evil spirits" that clung to my hands from the dirty wound. Maggie nodded knowingly. The germ theory, explained that way, made sense to her.

One day I had a small child whose head was covered with horrible green sores. The scalp was alive with lice, but had hardly any hair at all. A drastic clean-up job had to be done before I could treat the scalp, so I handed Maggie a bottle of strong shampoo and told her to take the child down to the river and wash him thoroughly.

When she returned the child's scalp was bleeding in places, but it was immaculately clean. Then I glanced at Maggie's hands. In the process, they too had been washed cleaner than they had been in many years. But that wasn't enough for Maggie! I saw her go over to Chai and hold out her cupped hands. He poured alcohol over them, and she scrubbed vigorously. Maggie was learning!

As you can see, Old Joe and the other witch doctors believed in the more natural drugs, like betel nuts, slivers of wood, boiled leaves, cow dung, baboon's blood, spittle, pig grease and incantations to the proper spirits. Old Joe had a most unique treatment for a compound fractured arm. I believe this tip should be recorded by the American Academy of Orthopedic Surgeons: The man with a broken arm is laid on his mat with his head facing to the south. The special deities of the orthopedic service are invoked in a loud prayer. Red, black, and white strings are tied around the fractured limb. The open wound is stuffed with cobwebs. The arm is then bound in bark. Roots are placed around this and a small bamboo cage is woven directly on the arm. The patient wears this for several weeks, if he lives. He rarely does. But if the patient dies, the loss is directly proportional to the position of the sun or the moon, or the number of evil spirits hanging around the neighborhood. The spirits and phantoms of these simple people cling to the cloak of night and fly on the wings of day.

One morning a lad came running to the hospital. He begged us to hurry to his village to see his little brother. We went, brought the child back and spent the remainder of the day trying to keep him alive. Cholera had struck. The child was a healthy, pink-cheeked lad at sunrise. A few hours later he had diarrhea. Soon it became severe. Then vomiting began. By noon his salt loss flung his limbs into painful spastic contractions. Never developing a fever, the evacuation continued in unbelievable amounts, the child writhing in muscle spasms due to salt loss. By evening, in spite of the intravenous and subcutaneous infusions of fluids, he had lost nearly half his body weight. He died at sunset. This was our first cholera case. Unhappily, it was not our last. We are veterans now. The Lao call this the "water death" because it comes with the first monsoon rains. It ends in a month or so, but the number of deaths in the interval is staggering. Because of vaccinations, the numbers slaughtered diminished just a bit. Imagine the horror of cholera if it would tear loose in downtown New York. Yet "there is only one child in the world, and that child's name is All Children." The Minister of Health heard of the cholera cases that we were having. He sent up several thousand vials of cholera vaccine. Our native nurses and midwives went out throughout all of the valley and vaccinated the people. The natives did the vaccinations so the simple villagers were quick to accept it.

The sick-call in Nam Tha was similar to Vang Vieng, though we had more surgical cases and during the early months the lines were a lot longer. However, in Vang Vieng all the cases were Lao, with an occasional Kha, while in Nam Tha there were many different tribes, each with their own ethnic characteristics. We now met such people as Yao, Thai Dam, Thai Neua, Lolo, Lan Ten, Meo, Lu, Chinese and Kha. We had to get interpreters for each dialect. Maggie could handle a couple of them. Our Kha coolies could speak Yao and Lao. Chai claimed that he understood the Meo, but I doubt it. The Thai Dam and Thai Neua speak a dialect similar to Lao. We all learned the Lao dialect with a mountain drawl.

Frequently a patient would have to go through four interpreters before she got her problem across to the doctor. It was not uncommon for an old gal to sit down and give her complaint to an interpreter in Meo. He would translate it to Maggie in Yao who would tell the coolie in Kha who in turn translated it to Kieu in Lao, who would tell me in French. I would ask Bob in English to give the lady something for her constipation.

Each tribe had its own costume. Many of them were brilliant with colors. In the morning when we would go to the clinic we would find clusters of these people, many who had traveled by foot or Tibetan pony for four or five days. Some had come to us from deep within Red China. The Yao tribes wear a dark blue headdress folded like a turban, such as exists in Arabia. Around this they wrap a large silver chain. At the end of the chain dangled the personal necessities like a silver toothpick, silver ear cleaners, a spatula for their betel-nut preparation and perhaps a tiger tooth or bear claw for good luck. In their ear lobes the Yao wear huge loops of silver, and around their necks a solid silver necklace about the thickness of your thumb. If they are wealthy, they frequently wear two or three of these heavy necklaces.

The Yao coats looked like the full-dress tails that we wear for formal occasions. But instead of lapels they had long rolls of tufted red material, not unlike yarn. This coat is worn next to the skin, without a shirt. It has solid silver buckles. Their pants are heavily embroidered with cotton in intricate designs. They are held up by taking the coat tails and wrapping them around the waist to form a thick belt. The pants come to just below the knees. Of course, they were barefoot.

The Thai Dam girls were the prettiest of them all. They wear their black hair in a tight bun. Into this they frequently stick large silver pins with bells and bangles on them. These pins also serve as ear picks. They wear a tight-fitting blouse buttoned all the way from neck to waist with beautiful squares of silver. Their long tight skirts are gracefully folded around their slim hips. At the bottom of the skirt there is a wide band of heavy embroidery, sometimes done with gold and silver threads.

The Kha Kho tribal women wear heavy rings in their ears, too; more often, their ear lobes were only yawning holes circled by a string of stretched flesh. These support huge-egg-sized knobs of gold or silver, their life savings. The Kha Kho men, like the Thai Dam and Yao men, frequently have a wispy black mustache, no more than a hundred hairs. These droop from the corners of their mouths. They look like Tartar tribesmen, but their soft eyes bespeak the mysticism of Asian holy men.

The Thai Neua dress like the Chinese with high mandarin collars, except that they added a white turban. The men of the Yao, Thai, and Chinese races wear the long classic pigtail of hair. It is said that the origin of the pigtail dates to the time of the conquest of this part of the world by Kublai Khan, who ordered all the men to grow long pigtails. With a cord of hair like this, a passing horseman could grasp it and lop off the man's head with his sword easier than if there was no pigtail to grasp.

All these mountain tribes are good and gentle people. Perhaps they sometimes hid a vicious spirit, but rarely did we see it. They are infinitely patient and possess qualities of devotion to family that are magnificent.

The new boys were improving each day, learning the things that needed to be learned and frequently things that should not have been learned. Of this last genre was the ability to start the "village symphony." Pete and Chai were the members of this late show. Late at night while all the village was in bed, Chai would beat his arms against his body and cackle like a flapping rooster. Pete, in another bedroom, would cock his ear, listen attentively and cackle back like a not-very-ladylike hen. Then Chai would call again and in a few minutes all the roosters and hens in the village would join in. The success of this symphony was directly proportional to the number of chickens singing. Unfortunately, this happened too successfully and too often for my sleep.

We had a great deal of livestock around our house at various times. At intervals we had monkeys, gibbons, parakeets, anteaters, a baby wildcat, a baby panther, a baby bear and other less easily identifiable pets. Our house also boasted free-roaming and not too pleasant rats and bats. The rats were the largest I have ever seen. You could slip a saddle on these animals and enter them into the Kentucky Derby. On the middle of the dining-room table we had a large tray on which we kept salt, pepper, catsup and other condiments. At night the rats would climb up on this table and raid the tray. We found it necessary to build a large wire-mesh to keep this tray covered up. Another time a rat fell into the water barrel and drowned; we found him there in the morning.

The bats were equally bad. They would circle our living room at night while we were trying to write letters. Though not vampires or biting bats, they certainly were a sickening nuisance. John decided one time to try to trap them with the wire-mesh cover that was used on the dining-room table. He did catch one, but this did not alleviate the condition very much.

One of the most trying things to endure was the inability ever to get away from each other. There was absolutely nothing to do but work and sleep. It was difficult to read by the bleating kerosene lamps, and the heat was too enervating. There was no local movie house, bowling alley, or bar. The boys usually spent the evenings making up surgical packs or writing letters. I always had a great deal of correspondence. I never knew that letter writing could become such a pleasure. I found myself becoming more intimate at a distance than I did or would become when I met friends face to face. In the quiet of a jungle night one can write of deeper hopes and fears, and perhaps bind friends with a tougher fiber of understanding than at close hand. I am afraid my letters were not always pleasant. They, like the land of Asia, were full of misery and wretchedness and nobility. Our life and my letters told of hideous death and the magnificence of a simple people. To those who had to endure these long epistles I can only beg them to "be to my virtues very kind, to my faults a little blind."

Along with numerous night calls another thing that prevented uninterrupted sleep was the frequent nocturnal visit of some huge water buffalo. We had a fence around our place and a wooden gate to boot. But the gate was seldom closed and during the night the meandering water buffaloes would frequently drop in for a snack of green grass. If a calf would stray away from the mother, the old lady would bellow and order it to return. A plaintive wail would burst forth from Junior, and that would start the chickens up, which would make the dogs start barking, and on and on. These sound like trival things, but they become mammoth when you're trying to get some rest. As long as we could continue to laugh at these things, we could continue to do our work, though sometimes it took dogged perseverance.

Whenever an airplane came to Nam Tha we became as excited as the mountain people. We would always run over to the airstrip. The French pilots who flew these small craft would swoop low over our house to indicate that they had something for us. Sometimes these pilots would bring French bread—a real treat. Their wheezing little planes were miraculous. They always managed to make it safely from Vientiane to Nam Tha and back, though it was difficult to think of one mechanical reason why they should; one plane was appropriately called *"Le Peut-être"* or "The Maybe." Once the pilots handed us a small bag but told us not to open it until we went back to the house. We were delighted to find bread, cognac and canned butter, and laughed at their note: "French Aid for the Underprivileged Americans of Nam Tha."

I can think of no event in Lao life surrounded by more superstition and tradition than the simple birth of a child. This is not unique with the Lao; in all primitive societies the birth of a baby is usually surrounded with a great deal of necromancy and custom. This combination makes very difficult any advancement into a more modern world.

The Lao calendar is not the same as that of the West. As a consequence, I could never take the woman's word on just when the baby would be born. Rarely did anyone know. In Laos the people believe that "when the fruit is ripe, it will drop."

All of my boys became good midwives, for them a talent of debatable value. I believe even Boatswain's Mate Baker could handle a delivery if he had to. Just a week after the new men arrived, I had to leave them alone in Nam Tha for a few days. Pete was breaking them in well. In Vientiane I received this cable: "All's fine, spent last night in labor, a boy for Bob and a girl for me."

John said that he was nervous enough during a delivery, but those sorcerers beating drums nearly drove him mad. Bob once spent twelve hours sitting and waiting, but after all, the woman had waited nine months.

When we were called at night, we hitched our miner's lights to our heads and bicycled to a nearby village. These lamps were like headlights that strapped on and had a long cord attached to eight batteries that we carried in a case in our pocket. The light was strong and ideal for the trail. During the delivery they worked well too, leaving our hands free. Sometimes we almost blinded each other.

There was an Oriental "reticence" to a delivery in Laos. It was as natural as God meant it to be. There was modesty, but much less than there would be in the States. All during the delivery, the family walks around the house, cooking soup for the other children, chewing betelnut, drinking hot tea and wailing occasionally to show their empathy for the woman in labor. The other family members where just shadows, but we could smell their presence and feel their body heat.

No statistics exist on fetal mortality for Laos but I would estimate them to be about like this: Fifty per cent of pregnancies do not go to completion. Of one hundred babies conceived, only fifty will be born alive. Of these fifty, twenty will die during infancy, from smallpox, cholera, malnutrition, whooping cough, or pneumonia. Of the thirty left, ten will die during childhood from malaria, trauma or dysentery. The twenty remaining will live to be ninety years old.

During a pregnancy there were many regulations that the mother must follow. Some were sensible, many were not. For example, an expectant mother may never eat bananas, honey or egg plant. From the time pregnancy begins she may not put on jewelry or participate in any Love Courts, Lam Vongs or *Bacis*. She was forbidden to sit on the top step of any staircase. (This last is not so foolish, as the staircases leading into Lao houses are usually just an inclined ladder, with bamboo rungs. Even I have fallen off these.) Every day when the woman bathes in the river she was supposed to brush her hair with eels if any were available. This is to facilitate delivery.

The Lao skirt is hemmed on the bottom with a wide band of beautifully woven designs, sometimes intricately laden with silver and gold threads. The rest of the skirt is just a cloth tube. During her pregnancy the Lao woman must never hang her skirt up to dry in any but the "normal position." If the skirt is hung upside down the child may present itself in the wrong position. There are certain invocations that a good Buddhist girl must recite during her pregnancy. Simply because she is pregnant is no excuse for her to avoid her work.

I have delivered after the women had spent the day decorticating rice, weaving, or working in the fields. This is good. Hard work keeps the child small, and with the mother being on her feet continuously, the baby is in a head-down position. The squatting posture of Asians also helps the pelvic musculature, facilitating deliveries. Primitive women have their children easier than others. There is no mixing of races here; no Swedish girl with a French mother and married to an Irishman with Scotch ancestry. Because it is a Lao married to a Lao, the child is fitted well to the pelvis from which he must make his exit.

When it was obvious that delivery will soon ensue the father called for all family members to come to the house and help. A birth was a family affair. The mother was put over in a corner, in a certain part of the house, facing the south, towards the religious capital, Luang Prabang. Some old snagtooth sorceress was the midwife. When she entered the house she was given, as an offering, a small silver bowl with three fruits. Later, when we Americans became assistants to the sorceress, we got the fruits.

The first thing the witch doctor did was to rub betel-nut oil, perfumes, orange rinds, and other "medicaments" onto the mother's abdomen and forehead in hopes of helping the obstetrical procedure. All the neighboring women came and sat in one part of the house chatting, and occasionally moaning, groaning, grunting and gasping, in order to help the poor mother.

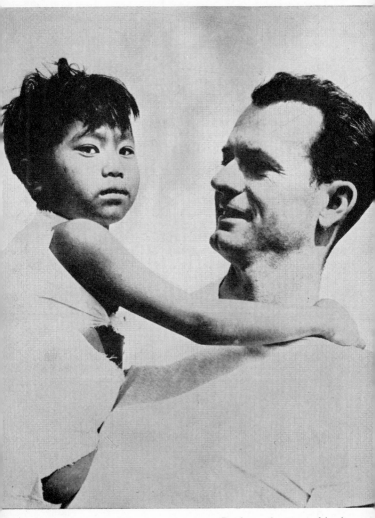

Dooley and a young friend.

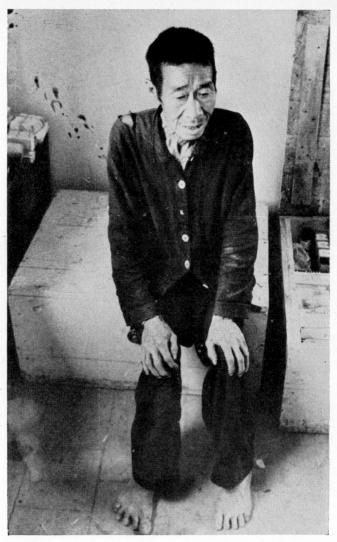

"Old Joe," a tubercular who turned up at sick-call daily, became our patient and our friend.

The mountain village of Ban Phu Van, nestled in a valley along the China border. It looks so quiet, yet it is on the rim of Red hell.

Here is a child not sure of anything.

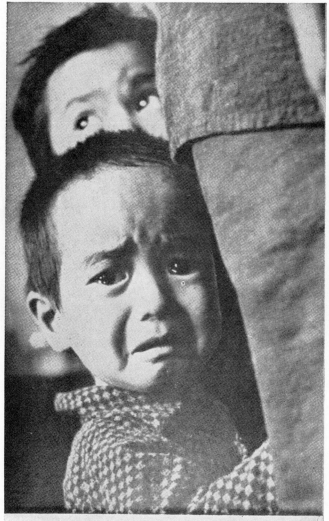

The ceremony of *baci*, with the old sorcerer chanting and our nurses making offerings and wishes.

Mother and child, dressed in a gift sweater from U.S. school children.

From some American friends, and well received, lollipops.

"Meals for Millions," along with Sustagen (the *"Ya mi henh,"* or medicine of strength, for the mountain people).

The protection of a mother is a universal warmth, knowing no national boundaries.

"The Great Float," a group of three *pirogues* or dugout canoes in which we traveled down a treacherous sector of the Nam Tha River to hold sick-call in isolated villages along the way. The two greatest dangers: rapids and bandits.

Norman Baker with a very dead jungle prowler. Notice Chai on his right, surveying the situation, wondering if he dare suggest that the Americans try a tiger rump steak.

Bob Waters dressing the hand of a girl who has already received her bib and dress as reward for good behavior. Ask this girl if she thinks Americans are monsters.

Mead Johnson's Deca-Vi-Sol doing its job for a soft-skinned jungle child.

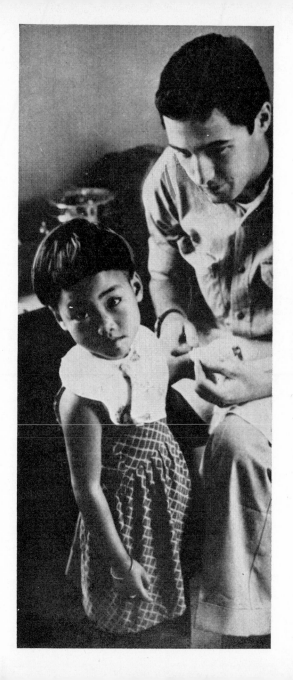

A child blinded by the pus of trachoma, too late to be helped.

The pathos in the eyes of Ion, wrapped in a CARE blanket.

Little Ion looks a lot different here, months later.

The men sat outside the house around a huge fire. The only men allowed inside were the wise men of the village who set up musical instruments in a corner. They lit candles, and banged on the drums throughout the whole delivery. The hut was packed to suffocation. The stifling odors that arose from the sweating bodies blended with the smoke from the indoor fire. Therefore the primary requirement for a new born child, oxygen, was a rare commodity. The mother's misery was augmented by the kindness of her friends.

The young woman was squatting on a small stool, clinging to a loop of rope hanging from the ceiling. In this strung-up position, she labored. The fact that she was sitting on the baby's head did not seem to register with them.

The Lao woman tried to breathe deeply through her mouth as she had been told that this will bring air to her child. The intention involved was better than the physiology. The crowd of family, wailing and crying, stole any stray bit of air that might have been lying around the hut.

The first thing we did when we were called was to greet the relatives and villagers outside the house, chat a moment, then go inside and empty the house. Only a few members of the immediate family, about fifteen, were allowed to remain. Then, with a minimum of kibitzing we could do our work.

We bowed toward the sorcerers over in the corner who were still beating their drums. Then we went to the woman in labor. It was absolutely impossible for me to lie on the floor to deliver a child. So we had the woman lie down. This always caused much consternation, but a grunt of approval from the sorceress doubling as midwife, accomplished the transfer of position. Again, much fuss about the direction of the head, the side of the house, and presence or absence of more relatives.

Chai took up his post with a large flashlight at the foot of the mat, issuing orders like Admiral Stump. And the people obeyed. We examined the girl to find out how things were coming along. We then struggled for a few moments with two or three skirts that the woman had snugly wrapped around her. Fine, shouldn't be much of a wait. So the sorceress and I discussed techniques. It was very dangerous if we did anything to offend these sorceresses. They have an important place in their community, and we could bring all hell down upon us if we made them lose face.

I would mention that the head was in this position and about this much dilation. Chai always explained that having a baby while lying down is the American way, and much less painful. (It is because we have given the woman a Demerol tablet.) Also some penicillin pills, and plenty of vitamins and iron.

As we had some time to spare, this was the opportune moment to talk to all the women in the house about various factors important to clean deliveries. But first there was a custom that must now be observed. On the woman's pelvis, over the baby's head, the sorceress had to sprinkle a little dirt from the earth. This is to infuse into the baby the spirits that live in the earth; the good earth wherein are the bones of their ancestors, wherein are the genii who shall come to the baby's life. I did not object to this practice. It would make little difference if I did. But I asked that they dump the dirt early. After they finished, I scrubbed the woman with soap and water, with as much splashing and commenting as possible. I pointed out that because the dirt of the centuries was the more important, it was sprinkled on first. Then my soap.

In our CARE midwife kits we have packets which contained a small triangular piece of muslin to be used as a baby cloth, some gauze and a cord tie. This was laid out, with as much sterility as possible, always explaining what we were doing, and asking if the sorceress did not approve of the American technique. She nodded her head in solemn agreement. We sometimes had the sorceress scrub her hands and assist us (after she spat out her wad of betel nut). Over in the corner the friends were still beating on the drums, the fire still burned, smoke was as thick as in a Manhattan nightclub and the odors overpowering. But we are beginning to stink by this time ourselves, so *"Bau pinh yanh."*

Anesthesia was unheard of. The mother was given a few bamboo jiggers of local rice wine and I added a mild narcotic. Various leaves and herbs were applied to the mother's nostrils because it was felt that a fit of sneezing helps labor. It certainly adds to the discomfort, though oddly enough it has certain therapeutic value. During all this time the husband was sitting at the head of the mat holding the wife's face in his hands, and blowing into her ear. Don't forget, the baby needs air.

During the last few minutes of labor all the women in the hut (and me too) would begin to shout *"bing bing bing!"* And the woman bings and bings, "pushing" as hard as she can.

The child was born, to the great relief of the family, doctor, husband and oh yes, mother too.

When the delivery was complete, the newborn baby was immediately handed over to the sorceress who was holding the sterile muslin. The hemostat clip was left on the umbilical cord.

In Laos it is felt that after the baby is delivered, all is finished. The mother is wrapped up in a clean skirt and put to bed. The placenta is ignored. As a consequence, hemorrhage is extremely common. We explained the error in this, and demonstrated the proper delivery of the placenta *"à l'americaine."* Then according to the Lao custom, we called for the bamboo. We placed the placenta in this hollow piece of bamboo and it was later buried under the front steps of the house. This is to bring brothers and sisters for the newborn child. The mother is fine, so attention is turned to junior.

Now custom demands the village elder to cut the baby's cord with two pieces of sharp bamboo. I did not object to this at all. We had learned by now. I first clipped the cord and tied it off with sterile ligature. From that point outward, the village elder can do all he wants. After he cut it with bamboo, he then rubbed ashes on the end of the umbilical cord. All this of course is distal to my sterile knot. Black, red and white cotton cords were tied around the wrists of the mother and child, invoking specific phantoms to come with their blessings.

There were then other rites of birth. A small ball of rice and pork was put behind each ear of the child. This was so that he shall never be hungry. The father wrapped the child in his *pakamo,* the sarong-like skirt. If the child was a boy, the father put into this swaddling bundle an article of labor. He wished him to be courageous, so he placed a small knife there too. If he had wished him to be studious he would have placed a writing brush; if a hunter, a crossbow and arrow. If the child had been a girl, a small gourd, or article of the loom, would have been placed in the bundle. The rice alcohol was then passed around, and everyone rejoiced. The husband gave us four coconuts as our payments. We kept two and gave two to our "assistant" the sorceress. This husband, as at home, managed to look as exhausted as his wife, but I think it was only show (in both instances). It is said that there are some tribes over in Burma that get the husband into the act in a more meaningful way. During the wife's labor, the husband is hung by his feet, outside of the house.

7

The Fellowship of Pain

Each morning I walked into the hospital compound with the feeling that I was traveling backward in time to a disease-ridden world that had ceased to exist long before I was born.

Ironically, I was always reminded of what the profs had told us in medical school: "We can now look upon leprosy, gentlemen, as a disease belonging to the Biblical era. . . . These yaws, dysenteries, and worm infestations you will probably never encounter in civilian practice. . . . We may say that the terrors of diphtheria, typhoid, smallpox vanished with the advent of modern vaccine therapy. . . ."

Ah, yes! But here they are—with others even more terrible —crowded into my own "waiting room"—the commonplace problems of any average day. True, this is Asia in the 20th Century. But not the 20th Century that western man knows!

Sick-call in Nam Tha was much more difficult than in Vang Vieng. Our patients were more numerous. The diseases were more varied, more severe. Ignorance and superstition were more prevalent. Traumatic injuries, often neglected or mistreated, made surgery a 'round the clock nightmare. Usually the symptoms were of the kind which are apparent to the naked eye. There were pregnant mothers, frequently tuberculars, carrying small children foul with smallpox or covered with sores. There were doddering oldsters with yaws, or swollen spleens, or wasting with leprosy. Then there were always the pathetic kids with skinny arms and legs, pinched faces, and enormous bellies.

We were often dealing with critical health problems born of colossal ignorance. These people have become so inured to disease, which is simply a part of their existence, that they speak of *kia tamada*, "normal fever." Malaria, for example, is a normal fever. Just live with it until, eventually, the spleen and liver are greatly enlarged and as hot as stones left out in the noonday sun.

They have lived on the edge of starvation for so long (despite the availability of natural nourishment) that their bodies have lost the capacity to store vitamins, fats, proteins. Only a few days' illness can throw the system into negative balance.

We pumped them full of vitamins, and passed out huge quantities of that heaven-sent MPF provided by Meals for Millions. I was often tempted to start hygiene classes, such as we held so successfully in Vang Vieng. But in Nam Tha there wasn't time. Sometimes it seemed that every other case I saw at sick-call required some kind of surgery, and my schedule grew top-heavy.

So we did the best we could. Sick-call itself became the classroom, and each case served as a lesson. Naturally a garrulous Irishman, I talked incessantly, but as simply as possible, for hours on end. Chai and Si, Maggie and Old Joe, the nurses and the coolies would jabber away in the various dialects. Thus, we tried to make the crowd in the yard understand why this woman or child was suffering, and how the suffering could have been avoided.

The people listened with wide-eyed attention. They were eager to learn. I could see in their faces what I am convinced is universal truth: No one really *wants* to be sick and miserable. Even the most "backward" people, given half a chance, will follow simple rules in order to be healthier and stronger.

So I think our sick-call "lectures" really did some good. Of course, the multi-lingual bedlam made those hours that much harder on our frazzled nerves. Fortunately, none of us had ever expected them to be easy.

One morning early in March a small plane swooped low over our compound and then headed for the landing strip. We knew it had come to take Denny Shepard on the first leg of his long journey home, back to the States and his long-suffering little bride.

With a lump in my throat, I asked one of the Lao nurses to take over and went outside. Denny had made us promise that there would be no farewell ceremonies. We were to carry on as usual. He just shook hands all 'round, and picked up his gear which was tied to both ends of a native balance-pole. We watched him trudge down the Main Drag, then he turned and waved before taking the trail to the airstrip. I would miss Denny Shepard sorely. He was a born doctor, and I always felt better when he was working across the surgical table from me. Now things were going to be different.

Pete Kessey was now the only one left of the original three, and his time was running out fast. Chai, fortunately, had developed into a dependable assistant. Thanks to Denny's tutelage he was now almost as good as any trained hospital corpsman. John deVitry and Bob Waters were catching on fast, and made good "circulating nurses" in the operating room. We had seven Lao nurses in training, four men and three girls. They were now familiar with my requirements. But I always had to watch myself in dealing with them, particularly when we were working under stress.

"Face" is a sensitive thing in the East. It means more than pride, personal dignity, or self-respect. With my taut nerves and terrible Irish temper, I was inclined to say things that would not only offend but cause the Lao to "lose face." And now I needed all the help I could get.

Surgery had become my heaviest burden. Scarcely a day passed without its quota of emergencies—a man who had been mauled by a bear; a kid whose hand had been blown off while playing with a live cartridge left over from the war; a worker who had virtually chopped a foot off while cutting bamboo in the jungle. But the cases that really taxed my skill as a young and inexperienced surgeon simply turned up in the line at sick-call. Some I would have to send away as hopeless. More often, and against my better judgment, I would say to Chai or Bob, "Put it down for surgery—first date open." Thus, instead of diminishing, my operating schedule grew longer by the day.

On the day Denny left, for example, a dignified Thai Dam tribesman came escorting his young daughter, a lovely girl with exquisite features, dark eyes, and perfectly groomed black hair in a chignon worn at the nape of the neck (indicating, according to Thai Dam custom, that she had not yet found her man). With an apprehensive look in his eye, the father explained that for years her feet and legs had been covered with sores that never healed. He lifted the ankle-length skirt, and on the legs were raised bronze plaques of tissue. When I say the huge, bloated, ulcerous legs my heart sank.

There were no knee or ankle reflexes. I took a scalpel and jabbed it into the foot, the ankle, then deep into the calf of the leg. She never winced. I needed no laboratory test to confirm the diagnosis. It was leprosy. We got at least a half-dozen new cases every month. There was little I could do for this lovely girl except clean up the secondary infections and administer palliatives. We didn't have the facilities for long-term disulfone therapy.

Then a man appeared with a wife who had an enormous purple tumor, about the size of a tangerine, hanging from her lower lip. The husband begged me to remove the horrible thing. They were both unmoved when I explained that the operation was difficult and dangerous. Actually, I had never performed such an operation, and had only a vague recollection of the procedure described in the textbooks. But the growth was already corrupt, and infection on the face is extremely dangerous. I decided to take a chance.

After several days on antibiotics to clear up the infection, the woman was given heavy sedation and a local anesthetic. I made what I hoped was the "classic" V-shaped incision, removed the tumor, and did as neat a job as possible of reconstructing the vermilion border of the lip. Since I had no laboratory for pathology, I had to assume that the tumor was malignant and trust to God that I had got it all.

Some weeks later we discharged the woman, healed and happy. The lower face was taut and crooked; but then I hadn't hoped for any masterpiece of plastic surgery. The husband looked upon it as a miracle. Later, I learned that he was mayor of a village some miles distant and quite an influential fellow in the valley. He did a lot to spread the word that the white medicine-men in Nam Tha were to be counted among Buddha's blessings.

I am sure that Denny will remember "Harriet." He has no way of knowing, however, that after his departure she became part of a beautiful and compassionate episode which the rest of us will always remember as the story of Harriet and Paul.

Harriet was not her real name. The boys had a habit of Anglicizing unpronounceable Lao names, and of bestowing entirely new names when that was difficult or impossible. This pathetic young mother, about 20 years old, was a Kha, a people who once were slaves and now comprise the Lao servant class—the humblest "hewers of wood and drawers of water." So they called her Harriet.

She came to us on a litter, delirious and in a condition too horrible to describe. I had seen women before who had been mutilated in childbirth, but none like Harriet. Even her bladder had been torn and her bowels ruptured. She needed many weeks of emergency treatment and pre-operative care. After that came a series of operations extending over many months.

When Denny left in March Harriet seemed more like a

human being. She was still in bed, suffering considerable pain and discomfort, with a catheter in her bladder and a rubber tube connecting it with a container on the floor. But she was on the mend when we placed Paul in the ward across from her.

Paul was a terminal cancer case. The disease had eaten away his pelvis and extended up into the abdomen. We could do no more than excise the tumors, and give him sedatives. He would improve some, then, in a few weeks, the malignant process would light up again with even greater fury.

Harriet and Paul required much more nursing care than we were able to give them. But we could do just so much and no more. However, out of the pain and suffering of these two miserable strangers, a beautiful and compassionate relationship was born. When the sedation wore off, Paul would moan and writhe in agony. Harriet would struggle out of bed, sling the catheter tube over her shoulder, and come to fix Paul's pillows, and comfort and feed him.

Then Paul would have his "good days." He would insist upon taking care of Harriet. Once, when he felt particularly strong, he was missing from the ward. The Lao nurse found him down at the river's edge laboriously washing out some of Harriet's soiled garments.

At last, Harriet was well enough to be discharged. She went to work as a laundress in the village. But she was unable to pay anything for all the care she had received. So, remembering that pride is strong even among the lowly Kha, we accepted her offer to work in the hospital as part-time cleaning woman and attendant. There she spent most of her evenings. Paul, who now needed constant care, became her special charge.

I was in the distant mountain village of Ban Phu Van when death brought a merciful end to Paul's suffering. The Lao nurses told me later that Harriet was at his bedside to the very end. They were as deeply moved as I was by the devotion of these two people. We had been privileged to glimpse the true nobility of what Albert Schweitzer calls "The Fellowship of Those Who Bear the Mark of Pain."

Wild animals created constant havoc in the surrounding jungles. Everyone had been talking about tigers lately, and the boys wanted a day off to go tiger-hunting. We had no time for days off. I would have liked a tiger rug, but I could picture a Dooley-skin rug in some tiger's lair. One day about dawn we were shaken from our cots by a boy jabbering something in machine-gun Lao. We heard just one word, "sua" which means "tiger." (In different tones it also means "shirt," and "buy.") We had visions of some horribly mauled child lying in a pool of blood. After Chai cleared his head enough to interpret for us, we found that the boy's father had just shot a tiger, and he wished to give it to us. With much joy we went to the man's village. He had bagged a splendid three-hundred-pound tiger measuring seven feet from tail to nose. The villagers pointed out to us that there were many nicks in the tiger's ears; they claimed that this was proof that at some time this animal had eaten a human being. I could see no physiological relationship between a nicked ear and a digested human being, but I did not argue.

Another extremely dangerous animal is the wild boar. When the animal sees a person, instead of running away he will always lunge at the individual. To hunt them the Lao find a narrow clear strip like a trail or a path. Then villagers form a line and, almost shoulder to shoulder, walk through the jungle beating their drums and yelling. The boar runs ahead, finally crossing the cleared path. There, up in a tree, the hunter sits with an old musket or flintlock.

One man had not yet climbed up the tree when a boar lumbered out of the jungle into the clearing. As soon as he saw the man, he attacked. The boar is the size of a very large hog and has two vicious curled teeth, sometimes eight inches in length. The animal immediately downed the native and turned and sank his teeth into the flesh of the man's thigh. The leg was impaled on the curled fangs and as the boar shook his head he threw the man about, ripping the flesh off of the leg. Finally the screaming man tore loose. The boar kept slashing with his teeth until he was finally driven away by the other villagers. They sent a runner to us immediately and told us he was being carried to Nam Tha. Finally he arrived, a mangled man who was almost exsanguinated by this time.

We had to tie off the femoral vein at the knee, so severe was the hemorrhaging. The man's right hand was mutilated beyond all hope of repair. We just cleaned it, cut away the dead tissue and closed it. No consideration could be given to any later function. It was just a glob of tissue and tendon. Antibiotics, anti-gangrene and anti-tetanus syrum prevented too much infection. Many weeks later the young fellow could walk though we had a difficult time coaxing him to extend his leg. It was still painful and there was some tendon short-ening. Months later he returned to visit us and was walking with only a slight limp. His right hand had healed all right, but it was completely useless, a limp appendage hooked to a forearm.

Such is life for the people of the jungle. I personally lived to a certain extent in a state of fear all the time I was in Laos. Fear of isolation, fear of loneliness, and fear of the great and ominous rain-forest. I believe that only a stupid man is bold in the jungle. The snakes, leeches, bloodsuckers, tigers, wild boar, bats, mosquitoes malignant with malaria—the presence of these quickly abolishes any primitive thrill of adventure and replaces it with an alarming dread.

As the months passed, there was an occasional evening when sickness and death seemed to take a respite, although never for long. Then I liked to wander around the town of Nam Tha, greeting friends and neighbors, and nursing in my heart a secret joy. We were Americans, our skins were white, our speech and manners and habits were different. But we weren't strangers or curiosities any more. We "belonged."

At the base of the big triangle which was the "town square" (or the Main Drag, as the boys called it), we hung a huge sheet, 180 square feet overall, between the trees. This served as our movie screen. Directly behind it, the projector was on the front porch of our house, and the amplifiers placed on a tree stump. Thus, on an average evening, as many as 1000 people, squatting on both sides of the screen, could enjoy the movies.

The peddlers set up their stands, lighted by flaming torches and kerosene lamps, along the road and did a thriving business selling Lao sweetmeats, soft drinks, rice-balls with chopped pork, and the strange bugs, bats, and little fishes that are rare delicacies to the Asian taste. Our movies had been a tre-mendous boon to the trade, and John and Bob grumbled that we ought to get a cut of the profits.

When the show starts, I stroll leisurely down the Main Drag. I pass the Police Headquarters, home of our body-guards, and greet the weary, mud-caked cops lounging on the porch after a hard day of jungle patrol. I stop before the Buddhist temple, a magnificent pagoda covered with gilt and porcelain, and admire the two angels, exquisitely carved from jade, that flank the steps. Beyond the Buddhist temple is the abode and shop of Mrs. PhoumaSassady, weaver, seamstress, merchant of sorts, and our benefactor and friend.

Mrs. Sassady has another distinction, which Denny Shepard discovered the day we arrived in Nam Tha. She owns the only Singer Sewing Machine in town—an ancient, pedal-operated model, but capable of wonders. Denny brought Mrs. Sassady bolts of linen from our stores, and she hemmed and sewed them for surgical drapes. She has been sewing for us ever since, mending our clothes, and making new garments patterned on the old. She refuses to accept payment. But, knowing that even Americans must "save face," she does accept an occasional chocolate bar. Bless you, Mrs. Sassady!

Across the way there is a line of nondescript and shabby shops, most of them lodged between the stilts of the elevated houses. But halfway down the street we come to the clean and well-stocked "general store" of Sisavath, which is attended by his young son, a student at the *lycée* in Vientiane, who is now home for the holidays. Young Sisavath, a handsome lad of 15 with a keen mind, speaks excellent French and a few words of American like "Okay," "Thank you very much" and (inevitably) "Atom Bomb."

Next comes the shop of Khuna, the village jeweler, a craftsman who works wonders with silver and gold. Money has little meaning in Nam Tha, and paper money none at all. Gold and silver, yes! But in this land of barter, even precious metal loses some of its basic value. So, instead of hoarding it, the people bring their gold and silver to Khuna, and he converts it into beautiful chains, necklaces, earrings, blouse buttons, and such practical ornaments as toothpicks and ear-cleaners.

A few months ago Khuna fell and sprained his ankle. In addition to the usual strapping, the use of novacain injections is optional in such cases. For some reason, I shot Khuna's painful, swollen ankle with novocain—the long-lasting variety. The immediate cessation of pain astonished him. He showed his appreciation by showering us with beautiful silver chains, bracelets, and ornaments. The boys were delighted. Then I saw a worried look on Bob Water's face. "How about that?" he asked. "Will the novocain wear off before the ankle heals?"

Near the apex of our triangle, where the trail to the airstrip starts, are the houses and shops of our Pakistani community. Jacob, Abdullah, and Ismail wandered across through north Burma, settled in Nam Tha, married Lao women, and fathered huge families of the cutest kids in town. But they cling strictly to their Moslem beliefs. When the rest of the town indulges in the frequent Lao festivals, drinking the local alcohol and eating succulent pork, the Pakistani remain aloof and adhere strictly to their own code. Yet they are congenial and respected members of the community.

Jacob, father of many sons, has a bald head and the long beard of a patriarch. Abdullah is a huge man with an enormous belly; I removed a fibroid tumor from his rear-end and he became my devoted friend. Ismail, a good man, has the dubious honor of running the biggest opium parlor in Nam Tha. Some of my patients are among his best customers—but they are also my most wretched and incurable cases. Probably they enjoy the pipe more than they do my morphine. Under these tragic circumstances I find it hard to blame them.

On the Saturday before Easter, we were busy with sick-call when two tall, rugged characters, obviously Americans, appeared at the hospital and saluted us with a hearty Hello. They introduced themselves as Pastor H. Carl Currie, a slim, balding man of about 40, and Pastor R. C. Hall, a smiling, crew-cut chap in his early thirties. They were both missionaries, of the Seventh Day Adventist Church. Pastor Hall said that when they landed at the airstrip some native had simply picked up their baggage and brought them to us. Where else would a couple of white men be going in Nam Tha?

We found two empty boxes and asked them to sit by while we finished with sick-call. Then we took them over to our house and started a conversation that continued far into that night. With only a break for sleep, chow, chores, and our prayers, we continued talking well into the Easter day.

The Adventists have a fine medical center in Bangkok, and several medical missions in Northern Thailand. Pastor Currie, one of the keenest and most devoted men I've ever met, told me they were exploring the possibilities of setting up a mission in Laos. He kept plying me with questions, and I told him all I knew about conditions in the central and northern parts of the country.

On Easter Sunday while we were eating lunch, we suddenly remembered a promise we had made several days previously, to circumcise a few of the Pakistani boys in our village. According to the Islam calendar this particular Sunday was a "felicitous" one for them, and we had been requested to perform the ceremony on each child whose age was on the even year. We expected to nip through this procedure in a few minutes. Then we discovered how prolific the Pakistani really were. I have forgotten the number but we did over seven circumcisions that afternoon. They were not all infants, so complete surgical procedures had to be done. Far after dark we crawled back to the house and just collapsed. Only to hear Pastor Currie laughing loudly. "Think of it," he said, "Irish Catholics eating lunch with Seventh Day Adventists, on Easter Sunday, performing an ancient Hebrew rite on Moslem children in the Buddhist Kingdom of Laos!"

The more I saw of Pastors Currie and Hall, the more I was convinced that they could perform a wonderful service for Laos, and I encouraged them to try it. Pastor Currie was puzzled by the Lao Government's attitude toward missionaries. I am happy to report that the attitude has officially changed.

One of the greatest festivals during the Buddhist calendar year is the feast of Songkran. This is held on their New Year's Eve. On this day all refuse in the village is burned, and each house is given a thorough cleaning. There is a belief that anything belonging to the previous year must not be carried over to the New Year. This would be unlucky. It is a sort of Public Health Department Cleaning Day, backed by a strong traditional belief. This belief is much more effective than prosaic reasoning would ever be.

Every morning at dawn the Buddhist *bonzes* (priests) bang on the pagoda gongs. This indicates that they will soon wrap their golden mantles of invisibility around themselves and go into the streets to beg for their food. With humility that somehow looks haughty, they hold their bowls in the crook of their arm and walk in long lines through the winding lanes of the village. In front of each house, kneeling on one knee, is a member of the family who puts some rice or some cakes into the bowl, and then says "Thank you." The *bonze* says nothing; indeed, if it is a woman who puts the food into his bowl, he cannot even look at her. The belief is that if one gives food to a *bonze* one is storing it for his own life after death. The *bonzes* are only the intermediaries.

But on the feast of Songkran the *bonzes* do not go out into the village. Rather, the food is brought to them in the Pagoda. In 1957 the Buddhist New Year's Day celebration fell on the 12th of April. Early on the 13th several days of feasting began. The long tables built at the Pagoda were loaded with food, rice, fruits, meats and a local orchestra played the khenes, cymbals, and of course the drums.

All the Buddha images were bathed, and the Abbot of the Pagoda was given a ceremonial bath. The young people of the village poured scented water into the palms of the older people, then presenting them with a towel. Chai tells me that in the former days the young people actually assisted the elders in their bath and to change their clothes. But this was too old-fashioned for the Buddhist year 2500.

The rest of the day, and for several after, the holiday spirit ran amuck. The strangest things are done on these days. For example, if you are liked, and someone wishes to express their liking, they throw a large gourd of water over you. Unfortunately we found we were well-beloved. As we would walk down the road a heretofore shy little girl would come out of her house and thoroughly douse us with water. But this is magic; the girl is hoping that we will have an abundant rain in the ensuing monsoon season, and this rain will bring a good season of cultivation. The pouring of water so abundantly over each other is a sort of wet prayer that we will have much water for our fields.

During this season many stories are told to the village children. Most of them have to do with water. The ancient legend I remember best concerns the mythical serpents, called Nagas, who lived in a lake in the Himalaya fairyland of Anavatapta. Their main source of sport was to float around on the lake's surface and spout water through their long snouts. This water would then rise to the heavens and fall to the earth as rain. On feast days these serpents were fed in hopes that they would be happy, spout a lot, and bring much rain for the season. So the New Year's celebrations in both America and Laos are Wet Feasts.

During all the various Buddhist feasts, great festivals were held. These gentle people love a party. They would have boat races, Lam Vongs, love courts, *bacis,* and the orchestras would play until late in the night. The balladeers would chant their sing-song themes of love, heroism, history, and fantastic stories of ancient legends. And I've a sneaking suspicion, judging from their grimaces, that they sometimes sang about the American medical team that had come to their land.

We noticed that many trees in the village had been gaily decorated for Songkran, while others were ignored. It was explained that the trees that were covered with spangles and baubles were "bo" trees. This tree is the symbol of the Lord Buddha's enlightenment, for it was under a "bo" tree that

Buddha sat in meditation, and received his third eye of inner vision.

During this season of the year many Love Courts are held, and this was a place where we could always find our interpreters and nurses, just as we first found Chai.

The supplies were still holding out, though I did write to Pfizer for some refills. They sent me all the more I needed. Meals for Millions sent me some more protein powder. Here this powder was referred to as "Ya mi henh." The vitamins, being a solution, were called "Ya mi henh nam" while the powder did not get the word "nam" added to it. "Ya" means medicine. "Mi" is "to have." "Henh" means "great strength."

The people of this country live on the edge of starvation. They seem to have no storage element for vitamins, fats or proteins. Only a few days of illness throws them into negative balance. Beri beri, a vitamin B-1 deficiency, was our most frequent complaint. Vitamin deficiencies were also the cause of much of our eye problems. Deca-Vi-Sol was given to nearly every patient who came to our sick-call. Meals for Millions was given to all who seemed to need "strength." This included the naked, shining, pot-bellied children, the pregnant tubercular women, and the oldsters plagued with yaws, malaria or other sicknesses.

I tried to get the parents to bring the children to me as soon as they became sick or developed a fever. But they did not understand this. As I have explained, they considered many fevers as "normal" and it was almost impossible to convince them that there was no such thing as kia tamada. By the time we would get the child he would be plunged into beri beri, if not something even more serious. The basic fight in Laos is ignorance, not disease.

In Vang Vieng we had formal classes in the village school three times a week. We taught the rudiments of hygiene and sanitation. In Nam Tha, as the lines were longer and surgery more time-consuming, we could not have these formal classes. But we held sick-call in such a way that each case we discussed became a class. All the waiting line would be huddled on the porch. When a child would be placed before us with this or that malady, we would instruct the mother on the care or prevention of such a sickness. All of the crowd sitting before the open doors on the porch would listen attentively to what we would say. They were eager to learn. They do not wish to be miserable. They want to progress and be healthier. They fully realize that they need not always be sick.

The best way to teach an Asian is through another Asian. We did this through our nurses and midwives. We taught them the use of our equipment, bandages and solutions. We taught them the way to deliver children without lacerations, infections or blindness. Then we gave them the CARE midwife kits to use themselves. We instructed the Army corpsmen with the small military group at Nam Tha. We then gave them the medical kits needed. Occasionally village chieftains would send someone down to us for a few days to learn a few facts about treating fevers or whatever was plaguing the village that week. We would teach, give the implements and medicines and send them back. In importance, teaching ranks next to surgery. In time consumption, it was about fifty per cent of the day. But rarely was it the lecture such as you visualize in America. We would often take a homemade blackboard to a village and gather all around for a talk about deliveries, or malaria, or the relationship between dirt and disease. But far more effective was the living illustration of a pathetic little child, followed by explanation to all in the clinic (and there would be over a hundred daily).

We once had a Thai Neua come to us from North Burma. This tribe live on the Western China-Burma frontier. He had a puncture wound of the foot which had been longstanding, and now most of his foot was one gaping red-crusted cavern. It exuded the worst stink I have ever known. All the tendons of his toes and ankle were scarred and shortened, and he could walk only with the help of a strong cane. If he had been a wizened old man, he could not have walked at all. We asked him how many days it took to travel to us. He said, "A great many." He said that our work was known even that far up in the western hills. Evidently our candle was giving a good light.

Every week Chinese came down from the Yunnan and Canton. They were really political refugees. They were living under the new Chinese Communist land reforms, and were being taxed accordingly. Much as they might not have liked the former regime, the new "agrarian reformers" were not living up to their promises. Though they had no religious quarrel with Communism, as the Catholics of North Viet Nam had, nevertheless they wanted to move out of that part of the world. Many had *parentage* in North Laos, and they would trickle down to this village.

The refugees I remember with the most tenderness is an old couple who came all the way from Canton. We took care of them, gave them blankets, medicines, and *"Ya mi henh."* The Governor gave them a small hut not too far from his. Weeks later this old Chinese came to our house and gave me a gift. As I was a mandarin, for my size 11-C feet he had made a pair of black cloth Chinese shoes about size seven.

A very rich Chinese once came down from Muong Sing, on the Burma border. He brought his attractive fifteen-year-old daughter who was cursed with a huge harelip. We repaired her and after her discharge from the ward, they disappeared into the underbelly of China. The Chao Khuong claims that he was a Red Chinese Army Officer. All we know is that he was very cooperative and most appreciative of what the Americans had done for his daughter. We transformed her from a somewhat hideous little girl to a very acceptable one. I think it will be more difficult for him to hate us now.

The constant escape of these people in China is symptomatic of the ulcer of unrest that is eating into China. Perhaps some day the sadistic murder, fury and fear of Communism will flood the land with too much blood. Perhaps the blueprint for terror which now wracks the land of China will be tossed aside and the people will revolt, demanding their freedom. Without pontificating, I pray that America will stand up and help such people in China as the relatives of the old shoemaker. We must. History teaches that we must. The cynic might say that the only lesson which history teaches is that mankind learns nothing from it.

Our surgery was just about as busy as any operating room of comparable size in the States. We once had a young man who had been hacking bamboo from the jungle to be used in building his home. His large machete-like knife hit a green bamboo and skewered off it, slicing deeply into his ankle. He severed most of his Achilles' tendon, with only a little bleeding. He was brought to us, and we were able to approximate the tendon ends and the sheath, and cast him in an extended position. Many months later we saw him, and he had regained nearly complete control of his leg.

Late one afternoon in May we saw two young people running across the compound to our building. Breathlessly they said that a child was coming with his hand blown off. Within a few minutes he was at the hospital. There was very little bleeding, but the whole face, abdomen and hand were peppered with black powder. And where the hand should have been was just a blasted blob of tissue. The boy had found an old cartridge in the jungle, probably something left over from the war. Just like boys in America, wondering what it was, he banged it on a rock. The explosion tore off much of his right hand, put out his right eye, and powder-burned all his belly. He was in the operating-room within hours after the accident. Because of the proper medicines, he did not develop gas gangrene, one of our most hideous visitors.

With Bob and John assisting, and Chai circulating, we amputated the finger stumps and disarticulated the small bones of the hand. We injected novocain into the nerve roots and double ligated the larger vessels. After a thorough cleansing we were able to close four-fifths of the wound, allowing just a small tube for drainage. Function was not even hoped for. We were able to get good results, and the hand healed well. For the eye there was nothing we could do. He lost an eye and a hand, but he was grateful for his life.

Just a few days later we had had a mail delivery from America and I had received one of the most touching letters I believe ever written. It was from a woman who said that she was "dying" from bone cancer but "no one tells me so." She said that the excruciating deep agony in her leg and arm bones was a great cross for her to endure. But she said that she was glad she had pain because she wanted to offer it to God in order to gain grace for "people like you boys." To me it was the power of her prayers that gave us sufficient talent, time and medicines to effect a cure for a little lad with shattered bones.

We repaired a lot of harelips. It is not any more common in Laos than anywhere else, but the problem is that the word spread around the mountains that the white medical team could cure this congenital defect. Sometimes we would get as many as five and six each week. Most of them were young adults, and we could operate under regional anesthesia, mobilize all the tissue of the cheek, and get a good closure. An adult patient is usually cooperative and cosmetic results are excellent. However, with kids it was really a fight. With the howling children we had to use open drip ether along with novocain. After the child was deep in anesthesia the mask would be removed and I'd operate as fast as I could, before the youngster began to awaken. Every few minutes I'd stop cutting while my assistants would put a sterile towel over the child's face and give some more ether. The children sputtered and spouted from time to time, but the majority of the repairs came out remarkably well.

Chai once told me that he had been in the market place and heard a child describing an operation. This child was born with a hideous harelip. He was thirteen before the white doctor came to his village. The parents brought him to us immediately, and we scheduled him for surgery. The operation had good results and the only remains of the huge defect was a small line scar. With much ado he was telling his companions of the procedure. "The white witch doctor, the tall one who talks so fast, told his assistants to pick me up. The two assistant witch doctors put me on that long table that they have over in their hospital hut. Then one of the assistants put some sort of charm over my face that looked like a piece of cloth. Then they dripped some horrible sweet-smelling magical liquid on my nose. I almost vomited but was soon transported somewhere else, like in a dream. I don't remember anything, but later I woke up in another one of their huts. My family was around, and they had a small piece of metal for me to look in. I saw my face like I can see it reflected in the clear river. The white doctor had pulled my upper lip shut and sewed it up like my mother stitches her sarong. Mother says that she watched them through the window and that I bled all over the place. They collected it in pieces of material and put it all in buckets on the floor. My face was no longer my old face, but a new face just as you see it now. Strange, these white men."

We had no electricity, therefore no X-ray was available. Fractured arms and legs were set by the touch alone. Plenty of plaster and buckets of prayers, and these fractures healed adequately. Gangrene was a constant threat. I remember one man who had been working in the field, and somehow his water buffalo trampled on him. His left arm was fractured, with both bone-ends piercing the skin. This happened in the morning. All that afternoon and the next morning the distant witch doctor did her best, with herbs, cages, cow dung, and incantations. During the night a foul odor exuded from him and dusky irregular dark blotches appeared on the skin.

That next afternoon she sent him to us. By this time gas gangrene had set in. The hand was completely cold, bloated and full of bullae. The forearm and arm were crepitant with subcutaneous gas. Amputation was the only answer. But before this could be done we had to attack the gangrene, and get the man out of the semicomatose condition he was in. The first injection of massive amounts of anti-gangrene serum caused no trouble, but the second dose caused a terrible allergic reaction, nearly resulting in his death. Again plenty of antibiotics, good nursing and adequate amputation, and he returned to his village alive.

We did have happier times in Nam Tha. One of the greatest occasions for us is the day that we introduced something astonishing into the lives of the village kids. We held a track meet. We laid all our plans through the head of the village school. And then dug up prizes. We held three-legged races, fifty-meter dashes, tug-of-wars, and other "advancements" of our civilization. For prizes we distributed every Hershey bar, pencil and calendar that we had. We even had some propaganda photos of the King of Laos. These we gave to the top winners. Then each winning child also had his picture taken with our polaroid camera. This was a permanent memento of his day of glory.

The anti-whiteman propaganda that the Communists so deftly injected into those villages along the China border was partially dissolved in our solutions of terramycin and Deca-Vi-Sol. But I believe track meets, village parties, movies, and roughhousing with the children helped as much.

John, Bob and I are Catholics. In the isolation of the north there are no priests, though on two occasions during our time at work, an Oblate missionary came to visit us. It was good to have our hut of a house transformed into a church of God during the thirty minutes that the priest offered holy Mass. I have attended Masses in the most magnificent cathedrals of the world, in many of the nations on the earth. I've heard sermons in most of the languages of Europe, and several of Asia. But never did the words seem to take on such a meaning, never was there such a profound depth to this meaning as when a small French missionary genuflected before our table-transformed-into-an-altar, and said: "I shall go unto the altar, to the altar of my God. . . ."

The physical layout of our living in Nam Tha was better than Vang Vieng. But it had to be because the circumstances in which we lived were ten times worse. Nam Tha was a village in medieval times. It was a constant task to keep our house in "livable condition." We had constantly to repaint, rescrub and rebuild. One afternoon a whole lower side of the wall fell out. These walls are made from woven bamboo, then a mixture like wattle is made from cow dung, rice straw, betel juice, lime, and some other ingredients known only to God and the natives. This paste is then spread on each side of the bamboo. The overall effect is sort of a smelly adobe.

Many say that the Lao are a lazy people. From my experience of living like a Lao, in a hut like his own, I am of the opinion that this is not true. Let me mention a few things a man must do. He must forge the iron, and make and repair his plow, carving the shaft and yoke himself. He must constantly rebuild a new harrow and blade. He must repair his house, weave new walls, cut thatch for the roof, repair the tools of the kitchen. He must keep his cart, feed his oxen, make rope and fiber. He must make hemp and weave the nets, then fish for his meals. He must build his loom so his wife and daughter can weave. But first he must grow, gin, mill and dye the cotton. He must care for the sick buffalo, cultivate his fields, practice his religion, and raise chickens, ducks, and grow a garden. This man is not lazy.

He may be ignorant, but a merely well-informed man is the most useless bore on God's earth. The Lao man has culture and expert knowledge in a specific direction; narrow to be sure, but nevertheless, deep.

If an American feels as though he is slowing down, he has many stimulants that he can turn to. Bourbon and water before dinner, extra caffeine in his coffee, perhaps a dexedrine or thyroid pill. The Lao does not have these. His food is humdrum and not especially nutritious. Glutinous rice is the staple of their diet. This is steamed and eaten with many sauces. There are condiments made from fish, pimento and other spices. The most popular is called "padek." This awful puree of salt and fish is the Chili Sauce of the Orient. In Viet Nam the same lousy stuff was called Nuoc Mom. Eggs are important in the diet. The word in Lao for chicken is *cai* and the word for the egg of a chicken is simply *cai cai*. Dairy products are not eaten. Beef, pork and fowl are killed only on feast days. On these occasions a local rice alcohol is drunk. To my buds this stuff tastes like kerosene.

Tobacco is grown, along with opium. When the mountain people are low on rice they go to a neighboring village and barter tobacco or opium for more rice. It is not uncommon to see a child of five or six smoking a huge cigar. Both sexes, at practically all ages, smoke their own tobacco, which is rolled in a small banana leaf.

Our diet was a mixture of East and West. We ate their

scrawny chickens and fertilized eggs with our C-rations. We ate our canned meats with their fish sauce. Once we tried tiger steaks, but they tasted like old tennis shoes.

One of the most constant sources of entertainment to us was the ever present group of dirty brown kids. They were around all through the day and most of the night, staring at us. Especially they loved to watch those bizarre Americans eat. They were sometimes sullen, sometimes bright, always curious. Some of the splashes of children would glare at our glossy white faces and hands, and jabber amongst themselves, while others would just sit and look. The Dooley carnival tent was not restricted to just children. Frequently the shy little kids would sit with their mothers and alternate their glance from her to us, and back to her for reassurance.

For a while we had a Meo lad who spent some evenings with us. This tribe lived at high altitudes; it is said that they cannot survive at lower than 3300 feet. I asked the boy why his people always lived on the mountain tops. He didn't know but said he would ask his father. When he returned in a few days he said he had asked, but his father said he had not the answer, but would ask his grandfather. The old man said that his own granffather had lived on that mountain top, and his ancestors were buried there, and he could see no reason for moving.

These Meo look much like the Tibetans, and come from the ancient Mongol Kingdom of Su-ch'uan. Their language is related to the Yao dialect. The Meo wear baggy light blue pants and a short, loosely fitting shirt that ends at the bottom of their rib cage. They wrap a brilliant scarlet sash around their waists and loop large hoops of silver around their necks, wrists and ankles. The men are solid and firm, and their bare midriff reveals a thick abdominal musculature. The French claim the Meo are the best soldiers of Laos. Every Meo you see is carrying a long gun. These guns are the old flintlock, and they carry a water buffalo's horn filled with gun-powder. The barrels are about three feet long, and the handle is shaped like a pistol. The whole gun is laboriously hand-made. It has been said that these guns are modeled from some guns given to the Chinese centuries ago by the Jesuit missionaries.

We passed many a long evening with youngsters like this sad-eyed Meo lad. We always loved to open packages and everyone, especially visitors, enjoyed watching us. It took hours to open all we might receive at one mail call. We would go over the medical samples, the instruments, vitamin pills, Hershey bars, and magazines. We learned that it is not necessary to have a bar or movie or a TV set nearby. The simple things of life can give us happiness.

One of the most maddening furies of Nam Tha were the teeming swarms of bugs that would infest the air. It was impossible to do surgery at night. When emergencies demanded that we did, the bugs would swirl around the light, climb into our hair and faces, and even onto the wound. Nets, screens, nothing we could contrive would keep them out. The atmosphere would be absolutely solid with insects. We had to turn our kerosene lamps out on some nights because these bugs would make any living unbearable. We would just give up the fight, get under a mosquito net and try to fall asleep.

Pavie and his friends, who shared our house, were constantly ambling in, sitting on the couch, talking with us, looking at the magazines, or just staring. They frequently pitched in when we were knocking out parts of the wall, collecting rain water, redesigning the house, or abolishing some of the room's drabness with picture-hanging, or catching bats. Pavie's babies would crawl into our part of the house, micturate a little, then crawl out.

One of the few visitors we ever had in Nam Tha was a woman. Her name was Marion Dix, a lecturer and photographer from Hollywood. She had heard of our work and had done documentary films on Operation Brotherhood, on Viet Nam, and other parts of Southeast Asia. She wrote and asked if she could come to our place. Months later she received the answer in the affirmative, and it took her only a few weeks to arrive in Nam Tha.

Most people were fearful of visiting Dooley. Many fluttering females would never have thought of boon-doggling it into Nam Tha. Many American men would take no chance on being so close to the Chinese border, with a chance of becoming marooned. But plucky Marion Dix left her chrome-plated Hollywood and, in slacks and a halter, arrived at the airstrip with a hundred pounds of cameras.

She stayed with us over a week, lived in our house and even used our shower (first and last female to do so). I told Marion that we thought she was a great gal. To come all the way to Nam Tha was risky enough, but to come during the monsoon season was doubly dangerous. We apologized for her being forced to live in a houseful of men. She answered, "Why this is what every woman dreams of!" She said that while cooking our dinner, so you see 'twas good to have a woman around the house.

Another event happened in May. Rarely did we ever get visitors, and the occasion was always bright for us. Even with the sense of humor that we tried to maintain, loneliness gnawed on us considerably. But before this visitor came, something else happened. We delivered Mrs. Cauvin's fourth baby. There was a minor scandal in the village because the child had slate blue eyes. The Chao Khuong was first to discover it and loudest to announce it. In honor of the occasion Cauvin gave us a bottle of champagne that he had hidden for months. This bottle of champagne had quite a story to it. He had a friend in the capital send it up months before and planned to present this to us on the auspicious occasion of his fourth child's birth. But more came of this bottle, too.

I must first explain that we lived close to the earth, close to the level of the humanity with whom we worked. We had no fancy things like big electrical generators, running water, hi-fi record players, or plumbing. But we did have enough to make life bearable and somewhat enjoyable by the new standards that we were forced to adopt. To be sure, we often yearned for stateside life. What was ordinary, now became a luxury. But while in the forest primeval, in a dirty little village, we lived as graciously as we could. We were clean, changed clothes for dinner, shaved every day, used decent language save for an occasional work-a-day word, and were a happy family. Of course, no champagne.

Mr. Bill Davies, a friend who worked for the Squibb Pharmaceutical Company in the Philippines, wrote that he was going to tour the distributors in Asia. He would be in Vientiane and he asked if there was any chance that he could get to Nam Tha. He was interested in the work that we were doing. Obviously we were interested in Squibb Pharmaceutical Company. I wrote all the explanations of how he could charter a small plane and fly to us if he came here before the rains and I told him of how much we wanted him to come. We loved visitors and so few ever came. This letter got out on one of the infrequent plane trips and many months later he arrived in Nam Tha. Bill stepped from the plane a rather ashen grey. His foot landed on the muddy airstrip and we immediately burst out in smiles. Here was our visitor dressed in an impeccable Brooks Brothers suit, silk tie and, as he said, "twenty-eight dollar shoes." Slogging through the mud he reached our house and collapsed from nervous exhaustion. He said he had never endured such a hazardous nor harrowing flight in all of his life. He said the pilot kept flying further north, and he was sure that he was deep over Red China. He claimed that if his insurance company had ever seen that airplane, they would immediately have canceled all policies. When the pilot finally pointed out the landing strip at Nam Tha, Bill Davies said that it looked no bigger "than my children's playpen."

We suggested that before dinner Bill take a good hot shower with some soft rain water. This would soothe him a bit. He was amazed that we had this accoutrement of civilization, but he quickly accepted and thoroughly enjoyed it. He then switched to some of our clean khakis and was in a mellow mood for dinner. We turned on the battery-run tape recorder and listened to some classical music sent to us by our friend Bill Donovan from USIS-Saigon. There were no commercials, no canned flap-doodle, just music. In honor of the occasion John and Si had prepared an exceptionally good chow. After dinner we drank the Cauvin delivery fee, that rare bottle of champagne. Although it wasn't very cool, Davies was astounded to find that we had such high caliber "luxurious" living here in the jungle. Several days later, not without some concern, the plane returned him to Vientiane. Many months later he sent us a thank-you note. He apologized for his tardiness in writing but said that he was busy composing an article for *Confidential* magazine. Its title was to be "Hot Showers and Cold Champagne, or The Truth Behind the Dooley Mission."

We were always being thrown from one extreme to the other. We would behave for a few minutes like stateside Americans and this was fun. Then suddenly some horror would make us again painfully aware of the rim of hell upon which we were balanced. Only a few days after Bill's letter came and we were bathed in chuckles, a boy was brought to our clinic and we were thrust into the stink of it all again.

That afternoon four Thai Dam men arrived in Nam Tha in near exhaustion. They had two stout bamboo poles on their shoulders between them and hanging from this was a roughly made litter. On top was a thin mattress and nearly hidden beneath cotton blankets was a headful of hair and the haggard gaunt face of a young boy. His friends and his brother had carried this boy down from a village several days away. They managed to get this crude-looking stretcher across the mountains and through the valley. They set the pitiful load before the hospital and we went out to examine the child. The first thing we noticed was how horribly infested he was with lice. He had head lice in his hair and scabies over all of his body. As we pulled the cloth blankets off of him, we saw a horrible sight. This boy looked like a man recently released from Dachau. His whole body was contorted with pain and frozen in this twisted position. He had a deep muscle infection of the left leg and had had this for a long time. Because he lay on his mat of a bed and never moved, all the rest of his body wasted away, atrophied. His left leg, the good leg, was no bigger around in the thigh than my wrist is. His knee was swollen and infected and the thigh and calf muscles looked like the meat on frog legs. He had several huge bed sores on his spine and back. He was so filthy that even as he lay there the ever-present flies started to crawl over his face, around his lips and into his eyes and ears. His brother kept constantly brushing these hideous creatures off him.

We agreed to keep the boy, Nai, in the hospital but the first thing we demanded was that he go down to the river and be thoroughly scrubbed up. Reed Carnrick Pharmaceutical House in New Jersey had sent us a shampoo called Kwell which kills body lice immediately. They also sent some ointment which, upon one application, will clear up a severe case of scabies. After a thorough washing with soap for the first time in his life, we finally admitted him into the ward.

The next morning my boys constructed an orthopedic bed. This consisted of a stout bed with teak wood posts around it and a frame overhead. From this frame a trapeze bar was hung. The antibiotics along with surgical incision and drainage cleared up the infection in a few days. The fight was now physiotherapy. Nai had many months of exercise ahead of him. We taught him how to do various exercises which would help to restore his muscle strength. His heel tendons were almost frozen in a position which made his toe point straight out, and he could not flex his foot upwards. His younger brother stayed at the hospital and cared for him. This youngster learned how to do all of the exercises and spent most of his day passively moving his brother's arms and legs. He also kept urging Nai to do it himself, actively. I believe it would behoove divorce-ridden America to learn of the devotion to family that exists amongst the primitive people.

Months later on a cane that his brother had made for him, Nai could stand at the side of his bed. Soon he walked around the bed though clutching at the wooden frame. Later he could get across the ward, and one day he called to me. He had walked across the compound and stood before us at the main building as proud as any boy in the world could be. And we were proud of him, too. Nai had conquered his disease and with his own guts he overcame his muscle atrophy. A few weeks later the boy who had come to us near death returned to his village. He held his head high, walked straight and well, and was dressed in American khakis, wearing blooming good health.

The force of kindness and love exhibited by my boys and by his brother redeemed Nai from ugliness and tragedy. The greatest bond among nations is faith in this force. An Asian brother and some American helpers, both taking care of a stricken lad, taught him how to walk again. Kindness is close to God and disarms man the quickest. You will never find this boy nor his brothers fighting against an American. They will remember us, with love.

We had hundreds of patients like Nai, boys we could cure. And we had patients like the girl with leprosy, to whom we could offer not even a breath of a chance.

All of our life was not fetid, however, We had some wonderfully happy moments, aside from the joy that came to us from our work. Some of our happiest times in our life in Nam Tha came from "Dammit." This was a pet gibbon that the boys had acquired. He was jet black all over save for his bottom exposure which was red, and his white muttonchop whiskers. Even the whites of his eyes were nearly black and in my opinion his personality was certainly so. There was much debate on what name should be given to this two-foot-tall creature that had been chosen as our permanent house guest. We drew straws and Pete won. On his not-so-very-broad-shoulders fell the responsibility of naming and caring for this thing. "Dom" means black in Lao. This thing could not have been any blacker. Dom can easily be debouched into dam. The "it" just comes naturally. The thing was named "Dammit" and will remain so forever.

His arm span was three feet, while his height from his toe to his head was only a hairy two feet. Yes, this gave him a slightly ungainly look, and the strangest gait I've ever seen. He walked upright on his legs, like certain Americans, but to maintain his balance he held his arms over his head, the elbows bent, with the forearms and hands dangling behind him. He leaned forward and tottered much like those little toys you used to buy from salesmen on the street. You set them on an inclined board, and they would waddle down it. Besides his gait Dammit had several other facets of personality that I believe worthy of mention. One was his great love. The other his detestation. His love was for Peter Sherrer Kessey, John deVitry and Robert Waters and anyone else who happened to walk past. All my men basked in the warm sunlight of Dammit's love. As for Tom Dooley, Dammit could not stand him. Rarely could he get near him, and when he did, Dammit would always micturate with uncanny accuracy.

Being beloved, Dammit was pampered. After caring for the Lao all day the boys would lower themselves to pampering this thing at night. The greatest treat was the weekly bath. I liked to see the gibbon being bathed because I knew that if the boys would only turn their backs a moment I could so easily have drowned him. No luck!

This bath water is not just ordinary water. Rain water was preferred, but sometimes the "harsher" river waters had to be used. The porcelain basin that we shaved in became the royal tub for delicate Dammit. The water was specially prepared, suds with the softest soaps, temperature tested on the flexor surface of Pete's alabaster forearm, and scented with someone's after shaving lotion (probably mine). As his highness' unshod feet would be submerged in the water he would give a noble kick or two, and then would allow himself to be slowly dangled into the basin, lowered ever so gently, ever so slowly. Finally when all the suds came over his shoulders, and his hands were under water too, Dammit would adopt a look of kingly disdain and contentment. After soaking, and several rinses in pre-tested waters, Dammit would be wrapped in someone's best terrycloth towel and rubbed down thoroughly. He loved it. Who wouldn't? After that he got a touch of after shaving lotion (too much water dries the skin) and a cloud of perfumed Cashmere Bouquet (which we imported from Hong Kong) powder to give him that safe feeling so important to growing gibbons. Of course such a cleansed and fastidious gibbon could not be sent back outside to be chained to the tree where he lived. Not after all that effort. So he was kept inside the house for a few days. Only at my insisting (and I *was* the Commanding Officer of this outfit) did they put a diaper on Dammit. They carried Dammit around with them in their free time. He would be immaculately clad in diaper, baby undershirt and looked all the world like some humans I know.

Pete had Dammit with him one time when we were on a village housecall. A huge snake about seven feet in length, and the size of my forearm, slithered across the road in front of us. I do not know the species, but probably a python. Pete jumped away, pulled out his pistol and aimed with the intent to kill. Dammit was in his usual position on Peter's stomach, with his arms around Pete's chest, and legs around his belly. Dammit screamed like a frightened virgin and clasped all the tighter. Pete stood there trying to shoot the python while firmly holding Dammit against his chest. I could not help thinking of those moldy paintings inside State capitol buildings depicting the early West. Especially the one with the staunch pioneer woman with her child clutched to her breast, her chin thrust out defiantly ready to battle the bitter winds and wilds of the West.

In Nam Tha we often used bicycles to get around in our village. The boys had built a wooden platform on the back of my bicycle so that I could carry my ubiquitous black medicine bag. On evenings when the weather was just right, Pete would take Dammit for a ride. Dammit would squat on this wooden board on the top of the back fender, wrap his lengthy arms around Pete's nearly non-existent waist and ride around town, with his chauffeur, majestically surveying all he commanded.

The boys built a house for Dammit in a large tree in front of our place. He had a long enough chain so he could leap all around the tree like his stupid ancestors did. There he would sit and glare at the "humanity" that might be passing through the village square. There was always a handful of people looking at him, for he was a sight indeed. I am glad the blasted thing did some good. He was a source of entertainment to everyone in the village as well as to Operation Laos of the International Rescue Committee. So deeply immersed in a sea of misery all around us, a stupid little thing like a pet can wield tremendous power to keep us in good spirits. It is pathetic that a man gets into such a position, but oddly enough, a gibbon can get him out.

In the jungles of Asia there are two types of gibbons, the golden ones called "Chanee" and the black ones called "Kang." Although they live in the same jungle together they never mate (looking at Dammit I could understand how the Chanee felt about it all). But this is a peculiar situation. They are the same animal in every respect save for their colors. Yet they would never mate.

The reason is understandable to the Lao. An ancient legend explains it. It is because of the good Prince Chantabun and his fickle wife, Chalernsri. You see, many years ago Prince Chantabun was the greatest Prince of the Kingdom. He was brave, stalwart and honest and all his people loved him very much. He was a great hunter and frequently fought tigers with his bare hands. The unfortunate thing about Prince Chantabun was that he was not handsome. In fact, he was very ugly. On a hunting trip the Prince met and fell in love with Chalernsri. She was a beautiful woman, but a commoner. They were married immediately and lived many months in happiness. They would frequently hunt together and on one such hunting trip they were stopped by a bandit. This bandit was masked, but he was tall and very straight and had about the same physique as the Prince. The bandit demanded that the Prince give him all his money. The Prince did. Then he demanded that the Prince give him his jewels. He did. Then the bandit demanded the Prince's wife, but the Prince refused and at such an insult attacked the bandit. They were evenly matched. The terrible fight lasted many hours. The bandit's mask was torn off and the wife noticed that the bandit was a most handsome fellow. The Prince nearly won and if his wife had helped him a little he could have been the victor. But the princess could not force herself to strike the beautiful bandit even though he was an evil man. At last the bandit hurled the good Prince to the ground and with a powerful thrust lunged his bloody knife through the Prince's chest. He then turned to take his pleasure with the fickle wife, who had sat idly by while the fight was going on, and while her husband was bleeding to death. But as he reached for her, the arm that went out was that of a black hairy ape, a gibbon. The gods were so angry at the bandit for killing the good and gentle Prince Chantabun that they had turned him into a black gibbon called "Kang." The gods were equally angry with the Princess, and they turned her into a golden gibbon called "Chanee."

The Chanee live all over the jungles of Southeast Asia and they can be recognized by their cry of "poo ahh," "poo ahh." This word means "husband." This is the punishment meted out by the gods for all the descendants of the Princess who would not come to the aid of her dying Prince. And for both Kang and Chanee the bliss of marriage can never be theirs.

The kids of Asia are wonderful. Here in northern Laos the families seem to vie with each other for the most fancy and different hair styles for their children. Some shave the head completely save for the cowlick, letting this grow like a pony tail. The Cantonese element in the north do this and then braid the cowlick. Other parents shave the boy's head, leaving a forelock which makes the fellow look a bit like a shetland pony. Some cut all the hair save a ring around the head, like a Franciscan tonsure.

The girls in the mountains never cut their hair. They let it grow long, and deftly knot it in the back, putting various ornaments into the knot. They wear long silver needles, decorative chopsticks, silver sticks with bells on them, silver knots and other delicate filigree chains. The effect is beautiful. Most of these girls have hair that falls close to their knees. When they bathe in the river, they untie this knot and it is a graceful and beautiful sight. They have no beauty parlors, permanents, settings or oils. In the north the Thai Dam girls wear their knots either in the back of the neck, or on the top of the head. If they do not have a husband, the knot is at the nape of the neck. If they have already found a man, the knot is on the top of the head.

While in Laos we all learned to speak the language of the land. Not fluently, to be sure, but adequately. Medical Lao is very simple. The word *chep* means pain. *Li* means lots of, or the superlative of anything. The longer the word is dragged out, and the higher the pitch of the voice, the more intense the meaning. All one has to do is learn the words for the parts of the body, or just watch the patient point to the head and listen to *chep hua liiiiii*. Although we all advanced to a point where we could understand most medical problems and express ourselves in the clinic, we still had a difficult time at dinner with the governor. Always the wrong intonation. For example the word *cai* can mean "chicken," "egg," "fever," "faraway," or "nearby," depending on the tone used, and the length or the brevity of the word. You can see how embarrassing this can get.

There were many clinical problems that I had not planned for. One of these was dentistry. I brought no dental instruments; little good they would have done, for I know nothing of this profession anyway. When people would come with loose teeth, like a term-pregnancy, the solution was obvious. For the first couple of weeks the Baker's tool chest was an adequate supply of instruments. At least for extracting. On one of our early visits to Vientiane we went to the Minister of Health who had given us free entry to his well-stocked warehouse. Most of his medicines and equipment were given to the Lao Government as American aid. As there is only one doctor by international standards in the kingdom, the majority of the aid medicines just sit in the warehouse. I was amazed as I walked down the halls of this building to find all the best antibiotics, medicines and instruments stored and not being utilized. We found the dental shelf, and stocked ourselves up with what we needed. Most of the instruments seemed unwieldly and all definitely unknown to me. Which one do I use where?

I wrote of this problem to a dentist, Dr. Karl Strobach, in Saint Louis. He sent back detailed diagrams and articles on just how to pull a tooth, when to, and when not to. He indicated the treatment for some basic dental problems. He later sent me some more delicate instruments which replaced the ones that we were using.

Dentistry then consumed about ten per cent of sick-call. No matter what the problem was we had only one Rx, extraction. Before each extraction we would give an injection of penicillin to protect the patient (though he could never understand why we gave him a shot in his bottom when it was his tooth that hurt). I believe one of the hardest tasks that we all had to become accustomed to was tooth-pulling. Afterwards, the boys scrubbed their hands with alcohol for several minutes each. I hated to do this job, so thoughtfully sloughed it off to the boys.

Our nights and days went on. Our weeks and months passed. The hideous skin diseases, the ringworm. the filth, the itch, the diarrhea, the leprosy, these became everyday visitors from hell to Nam Tha. The monotony of misery. The children with their pus-filled eyes, wearing rags for clothes, tattered and pitiful, these became "our" children; their problems, "our" problems. And when they improved, we too felt better. And when they thanked us here was our pay. This rich sense of satisfaction with even a small accomplishment. This is the way in which God sometimes said that He was pleased with our work.

In college we were taught the ubiquity of God. But to see God in all things when you are plunged into bleating materialism is sometimes hard. I certainly cannot see God when I look at a Mercedes Benz convertible. But in the jungle it is easier. Here we can know God a little better. Perhaps it is because of solitude. We can see God in the tropic rain, in the monsoon mud, in the tangy sweet smell of the earth that comes upon us as we walk amongst the mountains. The mimosa, the frangipani, the tamarind trees, the thatched roof, the quiet peace of the hills and valleys, the cool refreshment of the river, the surge of the night, the bustling of the market place. God is more intimately present in us than we realize. We ought to shut up a few minutes and seek Him. Life can signify much. We must just listen to the voices which are inside each of us. All we need to do is listen more acutely, rub our eyes and see things a bit better. If the light is seen, if the sweet odor is grasped, if the sound is heard, then a man's whole being is caught up in soul-satisfying contentment.

A man working in this world without tapping his own reservoir of spiritual strength is like a twin-engined plane flying with only one motor. He may get there, but it will be mighty difficult. Often, late at night, Bob, John and I would kneel beside our cots and pray the family rosary out loud. Our whole job took on a new meaning when we remembered the words, "Inasmuch as ye have done it unto the least of these, my brethren, ye have done it unto Me."

8

A Royal Visit

After ten months in Laos, I realized that I knew little more about the political situation than I did when I arrived. It was like living in a political Never-Never Land peopled by phantoms. You were aware of conflicting forces and of ever-present dangers. Yet it was impossible to identify them clearly.

This was due partly to the curious internal situation. The Royal Kingdom of Laos was a house divided against itself. The old King SisavangVong, ruler of the "independent kingdom within the French Union," lived in retirement in the ancient capital of Luang Prabang, but he had three nephews who were potent forces in Lao politics.

One brother, Prince SouvannaPhouma, the Premier, was striving to preserve Laos as a sort of constitutional monarchy friendly to the West. Another brother, Prince Souphanou-Vong, leaned strongly toward the Communists of China and North Viet Nam. The third and oldest of the half-brothers, Prince Phetserath, sometimes called the "George Washington of Laos," had withdrawn from active politics and was serving as a curious sort of peacemaker. All three brothers, however, insisted that their political differences were strictly a "family affair" which would be settled amicably and in due time.

In 1940, when Vichy France consented to the Japanese occupation of Indo-China, Prince Phetserath took the position that France thereby lost all claim to Laos as colony or protectorate. Then, in 1945, before withdrawing in defeat, the Japanese declared Laos an independent kingdom. King Sisavang Vong went into exile in Thailand, and Prince Phetserath became head of the shortlived (1945-46) Republic of Laos.

However, in 1946, France reconquered Laos, restored King SisavangVong to the throne. The three princes and about 10,-000 members of the Free Lao party fled to Bangkok. Later that year the French-Indochina war began. Three years later, the embattled French declared Laos a free nation on July 19, 1949, within the French Union. The three princes and their followers returned, but were unable to agree politically.

Prince SouvannaPhouma became Premier of the Royal Kingdom. Prince SouphanouVong became head of the Pathet Lao (Free Lao) movement and formed an alliance with the Communist Vietminh. Prince Phetserath, the "elder states-man," announced his withdrawal from politics.

Then in 1953 the Communist Vietminh invaded north Laos from Viet Nam and joined forces with the Pathet Lao. Under the terms of the armistice drawn up at the Geneva Conference in 1954, the Pathet Lao withdrew their forces to the two northern provinces of Sam Neua and Phong Saly, which are to be administered by the Royal Government "in collaboration with the Pathet Lao." Several attempts were made by Souvanna Phouma and Souphanou Vong (with Prince Phetserath acting as mediator) to form some sort of "collaboration." They had not been successful up to the time I left Laos in the fall of 1957.

This "family affair," I soon learned, was a very delicate subject in Laos. Members of the Lao Government always spoke kindly of the Pathet Lao as "our dissident brothers." They insisted that Prince SouphanouVong and the Pathet Lao were not Communists. Even in Nam Tha, the Chao Khuong would never admit that the Communist "bandits" who were responsible for the atrocity cases we saw were Lao. He in-sisted that they were Burmese, Chinese, Vietnamese, or mem-bers of the non-Lao tribes.

Inevitably, this kindly attitude toward the Pathet Lao re-minded me of the "harmless agrarian reformers" in China prior to the Red victory. There was also another point of similarity to pre-Communist China that frightened me—the political innocence of the great mass of Lao peasants.

The Lao people, particularly in the north, knew nothing about Communism or democracy. They were neither pro- nor anti-western. These were big issues far beyond their knowledge or understanding. There was unrest among them, and there is no doubt that this unrest was being stimulated. I am con-vinced that the Chao Khuong was right in suspecting the village "teachers" as the chief agitators.

But this agitation was shrewdly keyed to things the people could comprehend. It was directed against the Royal Lao Government, and against foreigners and, particularly, against the white man. It was anti-*farange*.

At first, I was greatly puzzled by that word *farange*, which is heard everywhere in Laos. People often addressed me as *Thanh Mo Farange. Thanh* means Honorable, and *Mo* means medicine or doctor. It was some time before I learned that *farange* is the Lao corruption of the word *français* or French. Originally it was applied to the despised colonial rulers, but eventually it came to mean all white foreigners. Our interpreters told the people that I was not *farange,* and should be called *Thanh Mo American* or simply *Thanh Mo.*

I was never able to find much comfort in the Lao's lack of political knowledge or their ignorance of Communist ideology. On the contrary, remembering China, I found the condition frightening. It meant that any political force—Royal Lao or Pathet Lao, democratic or Communist—that promised these people something better than what they had could probably claim their hearts and minds.

Suddenly we were told that His Highness Prince Phetserath, Viceroy of Laos, would visit our village in two days. Indubitably he would meet the American medical team. We were trying to steer clear of politics and now perhaps we were about to be thrust into it.

The afternoon and following morning the whole village was feverishly making preparations for the royal visit. They were constructing floral arches, cleaning up their lawns, and hanging out Lao flags that the Chao Khuong distributed. Prince Phetserath is a much loved figure in Laos.

On the appointed day, a little before high noon, the military, the villagers, all the children and almost everyone present in Nam Tha (including four Americans) were lined up on the path from the airstrip to the Chao Khuong's house. The Chao Khuong, Mayor and village officials were all dressed in starched white jackets that looked like the U. S. Navy summer uniform. With the jackets they wore purple knee-britches of silk with a fold of cloth between the legs, hitched to the waist in the back. Long black stockings and black shoes completed the royal uniform.

Noon passed, and several more hours. The children had broken ranks, so had everyone else. We sat around the little shack at the airport, wondering whether the Prince would arrive that day or next week. John deVitry was rehearsing Pete's French. Though Pete knew a great number of medical terms in French, and frequently could understand the gist of a conversation, he still did not exactly know how to greet a Prince. Neither did John and I, so we asked the Chao Khuong. The proper greeting was: *"Mes respects, Votre Altesse,"* which roughly means, "My respects, Your Highness."

Finally a plane was heard. All lined up in place again, the

Buddhist monks marked the area where the plane would unload the Prince, and we ran down to the middle of the line, and stood at our appointed spot. The plane landed, taxied up, and unloaded a few sleepy-eyed soldiers. It was not the Prince's plane, but an advance military guard for His Highness. Disappointment was manifested by groans, the Chao Khuong's being the loudest.

Soon afterwards another plane throbbed overhead, and the Royal Prince descended to Nam Tha. The spry old gentleman had on a felt hat. He was also dressed in white and royal purple, and carried a gnarled walking-stick which he did not use for support. He knelt before the priests and made his obeisances, then briskly walked down between the lines of scrubbed-up children. Each child handed him a little handful of flowers which he handed to his following entourage. They in turn placed the bouquets in silver bowls brought for the occasion. Everyone got down on one knee, pressed their palms together in front of their chests, fingers touching the nose, and bowed over their hands—a sort of a modified kow-tow. This is the way a Lao meets his Prince. We quickly decided that that would be un-American, so we would just shake hands, respectfully.

Pete happened to be first in our line. When the Prince saw his Texas face, he registered royal astonishment. He turned to the Chao Khuong who quickly explained that this was a member of the medical team of Americans living in Nam Tha. Peter, in the moment's fluster, thrust out his hand and said: *"Je suis Pierre."* When I heard him say "I am Peter," I had an almost uncontrollable impulse to add: "And upon this rock I shall build my church." The Prince just smiled. I said something (I don't remember what, but it was not *"Mes respects, Votre Altesse"*). Bob shook hands and said "Hello, sir" and John, the diplomat, with flamboyant ease uttered the proper words of respectful greeting.

That evening the Chao Khuong gave a small dinner. We had not been invited, nor did we expect to be, since this was an official visit of a Prince to a Lao village. However, the Prince apparently had other ideas and, at the last moment, I was commanded to present myself for dinner at seven o'clock. I had no suit with me in Nam Tha, just khakis and work clothes for mountain living. I quickly found a clean pair of pants and borrowed a coat from Cauvin. I had one white shirt and a green tie of my own. So I made my appearance for my first meal with royalty dressed in khaki pants, white shirt, green tie, and gray coat four sizes too small.

The Prince completely disarmed me. He was charming, extremely interested in my work, and did not ask me any of those "dangerous" political questions that I was so fearful of stumbling over. We did not discuss race riots in America, Mr. Dulles' beliefs, or Ambassador Parsons' politics. He did not ask for a frank opinion of his brother, nor did he mention the word Communism. We talked about delivering babies, raising chickens, keeping water buffalo off the front lawn, and instructing the villagers in the relationships of polluted water to diarrhea. We spoke in French.

I told him of our CARE midwife kits, and he asked me to go over to the hospital and get one, as he would like to see it. I replied, "Now?" The Chao Khuong sank in his chair at my lack of diplomacy, and the Prince replied, "Of course, now!" So around eleven p. m. I brought a midwife kit from the hospital. The Prince laid all the contents out on the table and went into each packet. He was acutely aware of a great many things that I thought Princes didn't know anything about.

When the time came to leave (I could tell, the Chao Khuong was staring at me) I made obeisance; standing fully erect (American), I pressed my hands together and bowed my head in the attitude of prayer (Lao), and said: *"Bonne nuit, monsieur"* (French). The Prince asked what time we ate breakfast. I said, "Around dawn." "Fine, I'll be there," he replied.

I woke the boys up at the house and told them we were having royalty for breakfast. We cleaned our house up as best we could right away, which was around midnight. Early the next morning John was cooking the best coffee he could make, and our interpreters, Si, Chai and Kieu were waiting in frozen terror. Si did not see how he could serve coffee because if he approached the Prince seated at a table, Si must crawl on his knees in order to keep his head lower than that of the Prince. "And how can I do this with a pot of hot coffee in my hands?" We had no solution.

Suddenly, at the bottom of the ladder, the Prince appeared, with his whole entourage. Should I go down the steps and bump into him? Standing there with my head ten feet higher than his, this seemed impolite even by American standards. However the Prince solved the crisis by coming up the stairs quickly, and without calamity. He then proceeded to examine every item of our place. The mats, the walls, our pictures of President Eisenhower and the King of Laos, the beams, the wash basins, the shower barrel, the bar, the bookcase, the boxes, the two "sofas," the medicine shelf, the kerosene lights, the Coleman kerosene stove, the odds and ends around the place.

Then, with royal aplomb, he sat down. John said meekly: "Coffee anyone?" The Prince did not eat any breakfast, so no one did. He gets up several hours before dawn every day, eats, prays and then goes to work.

He spied my tape recorder, and became very interested in this. We examined it, and I ran a tape for him, explaining that I used it to send recordings home to my local radio station in St. Louis. He asked me what I spoke of and I said: "The same things we spoke of last night." He grunted, *"Bon!"* He visited the hospital and the grounds, then suddenly returned to his plane and flew away. We slumped back into the house and collapsed on the chairs. The royal ordeal was over. Peter was still mumbling something like, *"Mes respects, Votre Altesse."* We did not know it then, but we were destined to see this Prince again.

9

Ban Phu Van and "Atomic Flu"

Pete Kessey's scheduled departure coincided with the beginning of the monsoon rains in May. The plane would arrive in Nam Tha around midday and because of the unpredictable weather, had to take off almost immediately in order to reach Vientiane before dark.

However, on the morning Pete was to leave, we received word that one of the midwives in an outlying village was faced with an emergency. The woman was hemorrhaging badly, and needed immediate help. I couldn't leave the hospital, and Pete was the only other person capable of handling the situation. Despite my warning that he would miss the plane and, hence, his connections all along the line, Pete insisted that he could handle the case and get back in plenty of time. So he grabbed a bag, summoned one of the Lao nurses, and together they set off afoot.

Pete prided himself on being an ornery, plain-talking Texan, which indeed he was. He was tough, raw-boned, fearless; but beneath his unpolished surface there were great depths of gentleness, compassion, fine sensitivity, and devotion to duty. The kids of Nam Tha loved him. Some evenings they would swarm around him on the porch, raising such a rumpus that I'd order him to send them all home, or else—

"Aw, whatthehell, Doc," he would say, "leave the kids alone. It's good for public relations!"

Pete never grumbled when it was his turn to be routed out of bed in the middle of the night to answer an emergency call. Yet it was always Pete who argued that I ought to take it easy. Often I would debate whether to go off into the mountains on an emergency involving surgery that only I could handle, or to forget about it and stick to my hospital schedule. Pete would say, "Stay where you are! You can't do everything —something's got to give!"

"No," I'd say, "I just can't let the guy die. There's a *moral* responsibility involved here." Pete always hooted when I said that; to him the word "moral" meant just one thing—sex!

On this particular morning, Pete's plane arrived just about the time the black storm clouds began socking in. John was waiting on the landing strip with orders to bring the pilot to the hospital where he could sit on him if necessary. The Frenchman appeared, arguing volubly about the weather and the delay. I stalled, coaxed, and cajoled, meanwhile praying that the weather would hold until Pete returned.

I was a nervous wreck when he finally showed up, exhausted but with a big, satisfied grin that told me his patient was okay. Nevertheless, I lit into him.

"Didn't you know we'd have trouble getting this crazy Frenchman to wait for you?" I demanded. "Why didn't you just pack the patient and leave the midwife in charge until I could get there?"

Pete looked at me with astonishment, and then he blew his top. "How the hell could I do that, you idiot?" he shouted. Then he began to smile. "Besides," he said, "you ought to know I had a *moral responsibility* to stay on the case."

We both laughed until the tears streamed down our faces. The angry Frenchman was gunning his engine impatiently when we got to the airstrip, and I watched the plane take off and skim under the lowering clouds. Good old Pete! He had promised me six months of his young life and given me ten. I hope he won't get lost among all the illustrious Tall Men of Texas. For lots of simple people in Indo-China, he'll always stand head and shoulders above the crowd.

As the word of the white-man's clinic in Nam Tha spread, we became accustomed to getting patients from afar. But I was surprised by the increasing number of Chinese. Some, of course, were refugees who had settled in northern Laos; but by discreet questioning I learned that a good many of our patients came across the border from Yunnan province in Red China. We even had a number of cases from Canton, which is over 800 miles away via North Viet Nam.

Once an extremely well-educated Chinese appeared at the hospital with his 15-year-old daughter whose face was disfigured by an unsightly harelip. He made no attempt to hide the fact that he came from Yunnan and had entered Laos via Muong Sing, an entry port on the Burma border.

The Chao Khuong was very suspicious of him, and insisted that he was an officer of the Red Chinese Army. Perhaps he was. I only know that he was grateful for the operation which transformed his ugly little daughter into a very attractive girl. If, indeed, he was a Red officer I feel reasonably confident that he now entertains some doubts, at least, about any anti-American propaganda he hears.

This case had another curious aftermath. The Chinese girl was by no means my first harelip operation in Nam Tha; but shortly after it I began to see an increasing number of harelips. It was publicity, I suppose, that spread my fame through the mountains and made me the first plastic surgeon in Northern Laos!

As the months went on Bob and John became hardened veterans, performing a splendid job. And Dooley is no easy boss. These young men had been quickly flung into misery such as they never dreamed existed. Neither had had any military experience, and were not accustomed to too much discipline. I would not tolerate anyone talking back, and ran my unit like a military unit. This they took very well, though thrown into it suddenly. Our constant awareness that we might be taken prisoners by the Communists kept us all on our toes. Military experience has proven that, in such a situation, there must be one chief and good Indians.

John's quiet diplomatic way of doing things was an excellent balancing lever for my sometimes impetuous actions. Much of the credit for the success of our last six months goes to John deVitry. Bob Waters, though not yet twenty-one, had the hands and heart of healing. Bob could not speak French, though he did study it constantly and caught the gist of most conversations. He was always studying medical textbooks and asking me questions. He became very proficient in operating-room techniques, and took over this command when Denny left. Both boys were capable of hard physical work in spite of frequent attacks of malaria, dysentery, and fatigue. None of these can be avoided when you live as we were forced to live.

Bob had a fixation on rats. Knowing that rats are intermediate carriers of typhus, plague and other diseases, Bob was constantly laying traps for them. Each morning he would take the caught culprits outside and burn them to be sure the fleas were killed. But no matter how many of these loathsome creatures Bob would destroy, more would always appear.

John and Chai became the closest of friends, spending long hours in conversation. Chai became a superb assistant and possessed the most important qualification of a medical man, compassion. With the dirtiest leper, bloated and wretched,

Chai was tender. To howling kids, Chai would manage a patient smile, and wave a mother's anxiety aside. To children consumed with terror of the "white witch doctor Dooley," Chai's reassuring words would bring them within my stethoscope's reach. In giving out balloons and toys Chai was the epitome of fairness, and when he went shopping in the market place he was sharp. Chai was the most important member of our mission, along with his phantoms, ghosts and spirits, with whom we learned to live in peaceful coexistence.

Time and again, sick people would tell me that they came from a place called Ban Phu Van, some 30 miles distant, high in the mountains, near the Burma border. Ban Phu Van, they said, was a progressive village, but with many sick people who could not make the long journey to Nam Tha.

I was eager to stage at least one sick call in Ban Phu Van, but the Chao Khuong, who felt personally responsible for my safety, argued against it. He said the mountain trails were treacherous, that the region was infested with bandits, and that the Communists would like nothing better than to get their hands on the white witch doctors of Nam Tha. Finally, he gave in when I consented to take along a number of coolies and several of his armed guards.

We packed our camping equipment and medical supplies on the backs of three little Tibetan ponies, and placed Bob Waters in charge. This main party was to go on ahead, and set up camp in the valley beyond the next mountain west of Nam Tha, where John and I would join them the next day.

The evening after Bob's departure a curious thing happened. I was asked to come immediately to the house of Ah Chan, probably the richest man in the village and owner of the only rice mill in Nam Tha. John and I ran down the road, pushed through a crowd of weeping and wailing villagers, and found Ah Chan lying on the floor. There was no heart beat, but the body was still warm; so we tried artificial respiration and I injected adrenalin directly into the heart muscle. We were too late. Ah Chan was dead.

The circumstances surrounding the death were puzzling. Ah Chan had been in perfect health. Less than ten minutes ago, he was talking and laughing with friends. Suddenly, without giving any sign of pain or distress, he simply keeled over. I arrived within a matter of minutes and found him dead.

Of course, it could have been some kind of heart attack or cerebral embolism. But cardiovascular diseases are extremely rare in this part of the world. Besides, **Ah Chan** was not yet 30 years old. I did not have the facilities for an autopsy, and I doubt that the family would permit it. So I could only speculate.

Ah Chan was one of the most beloved men in Nam Tha, and his death created quite a stir. While no one showed any animosity toward me, I could tell from the way people looked at me that my reputation as the great "white witch doctor" would suffer because of my inability to do anything for Ah Chan. The aftermath, however, was even more surprising.

The following morning, still worrying about Ah Chan's death, John and I traveled by bicycle over the 10 miserable miles of Cauvin's "road." At the end of the trail, we left our bikes in the jungle and crossed over the first mountain to Bob's campsite. The rest of the day we spent climbing up the steep trails to the summit of the next mountain.

The guides led on and we hiked up and up. We stopped once to chew on candy bars and eat rice from the hollow bamboo storage tubes. We had plently of water to drink and found some fruit in the jungle that tasted like raspberries. The deep jungle was magnificent, with mists of air steaming up from patches of light. At high noon the jungle was bright, but within an hour we were thrust back into darkness save for pools of light. When the sun shone directly down, it could pierce the trees. At an angle the sun could not penetrate and we were flung into a dusk-like atmosphere. We felt like small animals crawling on the jungle floor. The trees reached up with such majestic ease. Wild deer darted about and birds splashed through in a constant dazzlement of color. This seething, steaming jungle puts one in awe of God's magnificence.

Everywhere we saw the banana tree, heavy with fruit, yellow and succulent, shaded from the sun by thick fronds. There were monstrous fig trees and vines. We plunged into pale green glades of softness, a bend in the trail, and suddenly a towering wall so thick that the eye could only penetrate a few feet. Along the winding trails we hiked, then up another steep mountain slope, heavily laden with foliage. Suddenly we came out of the dark jungle, to the fringe of forest. We were near the top, and the air was ineffably clean and pure. We had a glorious view of the surrounding mountains, and felt as though we were on the top of the world. Our panting made us sure of it. The village was just a little further up, and we arrived around noon.

Ban Phu Van was not unlike other villages of Laos, though a bit dirtier. They had no water nearby, no stream save down in the valley. Therefore they could not bathe as often as they should have. The houses of Ban Phu Van were rectangular, built entirely of wooden planks and bamboo, the whole house elevated high on wooden piling. Their roofs were thatched. The beams, door and rafters were all very carefully fitted and tied with rattan cord.

These typical mountain houses have a corridor running along one side of the interior and the sleeping rooms open onto it. There is one huge room where all the family lives. There is usually a veranda on the side where the mother plucks her chickens and washes her babies. Beneath part of the house is a workroom primarily for weaving and dyeing cloth, for repairing and building tools. The animals are stabled under the main part of the house on the ground around the pilings. This odor is staggering to American nostrils, but to a tribesman this odor represents wealth.

Ban Phu Van was one of the most isolated villages that we had seen in Laos. It gave us an eerie feeling, as though we were not in this century but in a time-machine which had taken us back to Biblical days.

Hundreds stood around the house, and dozens inside. The air was oppressive and the stench of their bodies nearly overwhelming. We opened the chests of medicines, bags of pills, and the minor surgical gear. Water was brought to us in bamboo buckets and a partition of the wall removed to allow for some light. We boiled quantities of water, and laid out instruments for minor surgery. During the next four or five hours, with the help of Chai, Bob, and John, I treated about 150 sick people.

The local schoolteacher, an intelligent young man named Phya Vong, remained by my side during sick-call. He told us that he was born in the village, but had gone to school in North Viet Nam in 1954. This interested me because it is standard procedure for the Communists to select the brightest boy in each remote village, give him some brief training (or indoctrination) in China or North Viet Nam, and then send him back home as a teacher. The Chao Khuong always insisted that these "teachers" were the most active Communist agents in northern Laos.

Phya Vong, who spoke French well, was cooperative and utterly charming. But he would not be drawn into any discussion of politics. Since he was by far the best educated man in the village, I left a substantial supply of basic medicines with him, and he promised to send seriously sick people to the clinic in Nam Tha in the future. I had no idea of how he really felt toward us; but, at least, like the rest of the villagers, he knew now that all white men are not monsters.

On the way back, near the bottom of the valley, a man stopped us. He asked us to visit his child who was sick "in the head." It was only off the trail a bit, and there were less than ten huts in his village. We agreed. He walked ahead swiftly, determined, and frightened. Finally we came to his near-dead village. Inside his hut I crept past an oil lamp, and then he pointed to a pool of darkness. He said *"ni."* There was his son. A child of about four, he was whimpering like a wretched little dog. On examination I found he had some sort of cerebral spasticity and complete muscle atrophy. His legs and arms were little knobby rods and his bloated stomach bespoke heavy worm infestation. He was lying on a mat soaked with his own urine. He had no contact with reality and had definite signs of cerebral damage.

There was absolutely nothing that I could do. Nor could I think of anything in all the chests of hope that even a sterile American Medical Center could offer to this lad. I explained as best I could. The father accepted my verdict with philosophical understanding. I, the white witch doctor, was absolutely his last hope for his son. Remembering I should never rob a patient of his last hope, I was apprehensive about painting the true totally black picture. I tried to leave a little light, but conscience forbade me to offer much. The father said that there were several in the village like this. Later when I discussed it with John and Bob, we decided that this must be a familial thing.

It was not yet dark when we arrived at the camp where we had left the bicycles. Remembering Bob's tale of trying to sleep in the jungle campsite the night before, we decided that we three would ride our bicycles back to Nam Tha. The coolies and Kieu could return the next day with the horses. It was still an hour or so before nightfall, so we felt we would be able to make it. For the first hour we pumped up and coasted down. We were speeding as much as our aching legs would let us. The road was dry, though occasionally we would hit a puddle.

At one spot we were coasting down too fast, considering the rough narrowness of the road. There was a drop of several hundred feet off the side of this path. While shooting around a corner I lost control of my bicycle. The tires slid on the trail and I was flung over the handlebars. I skidded on my belly across the road surface, directly toward the edge of the cliff. I remember throwing my arms out in front of me, digging my hands into the road to brake myself. That's all I remember.

I was unconscious for only a moment. When I came to I was perched on the edge of the trail, but still on it. I had deep abrasions along my chest and stomach, and the front of my shirt was a dirty mixture of blood and dust. I looked at my hand and to my horror found my left thumb protruding out at a right angle of my wrist. It was dislocated and a wrist bone was fractured. I remembered what to do, and pulled on it, slowly, as hard as I could. With a swift excruciating pain, it slipped back into place.

By that time Bob and John were around the corner and had to skid to a stop to keep from running over my tangled bike. All they could do was comment, "Lucky you didn't go over the edge." Suddenly we both realized something. I would have to get to a doctor and to an X-ray machine. But I was the only doctor around, and we had no X-ray.

A physician is taught never to self-medicate. In this case however, self-reduction of a fracture-dislocation was imperative. To a man whose hands are as important to his livelihood as a doctor's, this kind of injury seemed ghastly. However, the fracture-dislocation of Dr. Tom Dooley on the path to Ban Phu Van was a very minor footnote in the history of Operation Laos.

The bicycle was bent up a bit, but we pounded it straight. I had the small medical kit on the back of my bike and found a large Ace elastic bandage to wrap my rapidly swelling hand in. We then went on. During the last thirty minutes of the trip it rained heavily.

It was dusk when we arrived at Nam Tha. Si was sitting on the top stair waiting for us. The lad had a premonition that we would be back a day early. Never did our house look so good as that twilight moment when we returned. We made a pathetic sight. I was bloodstained and muddy, my hand in a big bandage. Bob was so tired and sore and bug bitten that he could hardly crawl. John was numb with fatigue. We lay on the floor for an hour or so, with Si serving us coffee off the mat. Finally we took turns at the shower, and collapsed in bed. My hand was throbbing and swelling, and I was trying to decide how I would ever get to an X-ray machine. I never did. A posterior plaster cast, the luck of the Irish, and the grace of God produced good approximation and a functioning joint.

The next morning we got to the hospital early, and found the whole town excited by the lavish plans for Ah Chan's funeral and, more surprising, aghast over the "cause" of Ah Chan's death.

Everyone in Nam Tha now knew that Ah Chan had died of something called *kia atomique* (atomic fever) which can be translated roughly as Atomic Flu! The Chao Khuong himself was the first to tell us about it. Of course, he said, the story was absurd. He knew that no fever or influenza could kill with such lightning speed. But, he said, the rumor had spread like wildfire, and everyone else believed it!

How had the rumor started? I'll never know. There were only two or three radio sets in all Nam Tha. Si, our houseboy, swore that the report had not been on Radio Peking (which was the only station we could get on our small set); and the Chao Khuong, who had the only powerful receiver in the province, said he had never heard *kia atomique* mentioned on any broadcast.

Ah Chan's funeral lasted nine days. Runners had been sent out with the news, and friends and relatives from the most remote villages had gathered in Nam Tha. The long period of mourning was more grotesque even than an old-fashioned Irish wake. The Buddhist *bonzes* (monks) prayed and burned joss sticks, the mourners wailed, the musicians twanged their stringed instruments and clashed cymbals, and the feasting and drinking went on far into the night. Finally, on the ninth day, Ah Chan's coffin was placed high on a wooden platform, with the head toward Luang Prabang, the ancient religious capital of Laos, and the funeral pyre was lighted.

But the buzz-buzz about *kia atomique* didn't die with the flames. Strangely, at that moment, in June 1957, the western world was worrying about Asian Flu. Yet in this remote corner of the Far East, practically cut off from the lines of world communication, someone had dreamed up a counterpart that was Made in America. To me this was a masterpiece of subtle propaganda—and a telling blow at the White-Man's Medicine which, apparently, was getting to be too popular in Nam Tha.

This series of events—Ah Chan's unexplained death; the dying mountain child near Ban Phu Van, in whose presence

I felt absolutely hopeless; the injury to my hand; the fatigue of our journey; the feeling of frustration at the smallness of our accomplishment and the enormity of the task, the millions we could not treat—brought me almost to the brink of despair. Then a letter arrived and it was just what I needed.

It was from Dr. Melvin Casberg, the former dean of my medical school. He wrote: "Tom, you will face periods of abject discouragement, when all your efforts will appear negligible in the face of such a tremendous task. But remember, Tom, one can trace all major steps in the progress of humanity to the individual, to the minority. So keep up your courage, and as Saint Paul said so many years ago, 'Be steadfast in faith.'"

10

The Great Float

The "Great Float" was John deVitry's idea. As the time for "phasing out" of Nam Tha approached, he argued that instead of going directly to Vientiane we ought to travel down the Nam Tha River in small boats holding sick-call in the isolated villages along the way.

The Chao Khuong was violently opposed to the scheme. He insisted that the river was treacherous and impassable, and that the people in the isolated villages were hostile to white men. Most of the political prisoners in his stockade, he said, came from this region, yet his soldiers did not dare venture more than a few miles down the river for mopping-up operations. Moreover, he doubted that we could find boatmen who would risk their necks on the trip.

I sent a message to Dr. Oudom, and he promptly sent back his approval. The old Governor threw up his hands, and said he was no longer responsible. However, he did insist upon sending out a party of armed guards in advance, and assigned four gun-toting guards to accompany us.

We were to travel in *pirogues,* dugout canoes about 12 feet long, which were the only boats capable of shooting the rapids. As the Governor predicted, we had plenty of trouble signing up the boatmen. No one had ever made the trip before; and, in addition to bandits and impassable rapids, we would have to contend with the heavy rains of the monsoon season. However, extra pay plus some persuasion by the Chao Khuong prevailed.

John lined up three *pirogues,* each with a crew of four men. Two men sat in the middle of the dugout and paddled; the others mounted the "flying platforms" fore and aft and used the long oars for steering. We carefully divided our medical supplies, food, and camping equipment among the three boats, so that if one was lost we would still be able to eat, sleep and hold sick-call.

The departure time was set at dawn, but following the usual Lao pattern we heaved anchor a little before lunchtime. We were ready to go and were down at the *pirogues* with our equipment. The chief boatman was to come down in just a few minutes. An hour later he ambled down, took a look at us, and then said that he would have to go back to the Chao Khuong to get a paper of some sort. The interpreters said that they were afraid the boatmen were getting cold feet; they knew the banditry and the river and demanded more money for such a risky trip. I cannot say I blamed them.

When they finally returned from the Governor's, we said another farewell to our dozen friends who were squatting under a tree trying to avoid the constant drizzle. I squatted inside the little bamboo hut in the middle of this long dugout and when the boatman got aboard I yelled in good Navy style, "Heave anchor," but we did not heave anchor. The chief boatman did not like the way his assistants, and the Americans, had loaded the canoes.

We then had to unpack and rearrange all the gear following the boatman's orders concerning weights, and my orders concerning value of equipment. Finally we seemed to be loaded properly and, without adieu, we sort of drifted away from the shore. It was pouring in torrents by this time; it did not stop for the next four days. We waved a listless goodbye to our dampened friends.

That first afternoon's float, as we blithely refer to rapid shooting, was as frightening as it was interesting. One boatman stood on the bow of the slender dugout and one on the stern, each with a huge paddle for steering. Two other men squatted just inboard of them with short oars, used for thrusting us along. They did not have to stroke very much because the Nam Tha River current took care of us, propelling us with alternating heaves.

Anticipating that the cargo was tender, to say nothing of us, the boatmen wove a palm leaf covering which allowed us to sit, hunched over on the wet floor of the canoe, and just fit our heads under this curved roof. But during the incessant rains even this was a blessing. However, it did not take long for the rain to break through the leaves and we were just as wet inside as we were out.

Our first stop was about three hours down the river. The boatmen got out and waded into the jungle to hack down some more of these large green bamboo logs to attach to the side of the boat. This is because we were rocking so very badly and the rapids were more severe than he had anticipated. The river here had no bank. The monsoon-flooded waters had risen so high that there were large bushes and trees smack in the middle of the river, and the edges were not banks at all but simply trees on which the water had climbed up several feet. When we came to the first rapid of any size, the *pirogues* pulled over to the side once again.

This time we had to get out with the most valuable equipment, and plunge through the deep jungle on foot. We walked along the side of the river while the boats shot the rough part of the rapid, bouncing off of rocks, between logs and over the wild, white foam. Suddenly they came out into a small, quiet whirlpool and were able to paddle over to the edge where we were standing, knee-deep in water, with camera and gear over our heads—as the rain poured down on them. And so passed our first day, stopping, diving along the edge of the rapid, getting back aboard again, and that constant, drenching, chilly monsoon rain.

The first night we reached a small village where only a few old women could be found. With four gun-toting guards we looked more like an invading force than a benevolent medical mission. The somewhat frightened women told us that the menfolk were in the jungle hunting but would be back later. We said that all we wanted to do was get into an empty or abandoned hut, dry off, and eat. We were shown the village guest house, a miserable one. We somehow washed up, dried around the fire, heated up some C-rations and promptly tied up the mosquito nets, unrolled the bedding and fell into the dry warm arms of Morpheus, dreaming of martinis and hard, hard land.

The next morning I woke up to the sound of all the village mulling around our hut. We had no fear because this village was still close enough to Nam Tha that we knew many here had been to our hospital. Some we recognized as old patients. There were not too many people here who needed medicine because they frequently came on to Nam Tha.

Although the weather remained unchanged the trip became ten times more interesting. We were plunging down deep gorges, but instead of Colorado River-like cliffs on each side, we were closed in by huge luxuriant jungle giants. I was constantly yelling to the boys in the other boat, and they were calling back to me: "Look at that animal!" "Did you see that, was it a bird? Was it a monkey?"

We stopped at several villages that day and at one we ate our C-ration lunch. Each village along this river seemed to have its own epidemic. None of the epidemics seemed to cross or go up and down the river. These villages live in complete isolation from one another with no commerce and no trading. Although this is evil, as far as progress is concerned, it is good insofar as it prevents the spread of epidemic diseases. In some villages there was cholera, in others dysentery. Everywhere there were scabies, ringworm, beri beri, the alternating fevers of malaria, intestinal worms and yaws. I will never get hardened to this misery.

In the village where we planned to spend our second night, we thought the propagandists might have made some headway and we were a bit apprehensive. It was a poor village and extremely isolated, even from Nam Tha. As we walked up the side of the jungle into the cleared area where the village stood, clinging to the mountain slope, we asked for the house of the chieftain. We were given directions and all the village stirred and walked behind us. Suddenly from the crowd a man stepped forward with his small son. The father, evidently an important man in the village, came up to us, fell on his knees, clasped his hands before his face and thanked us again for what we had done. He then welcomed us to his village. His son had been one of the first cases of Kwashiorkor's disease that we had in Nam Tha. We had cured him and were able to explain to his father how to prevent a relapse. The son walked up to John and put his arms around John's waist. He had absolutely no fear, for he had known the tenderness and compassion of my boys. This made us acceptable to the village immediately, and the Tassieng came to the top of his stairs and beckoned us to enter into his home.

This Tassieng was a grand old fellow and answered a lot of questions for us. We asked him if he had ever seen white men here before. "No." We asked if he, or his family who were sitting around, found us droll. His truthful answer was, "Yes." As the evening progressed we became more interesting to them and they to us. We asked him if he had ever seen Chinese in this village. The old man said, "Oh, yes. Chinese have come here frequently, but not recently." I asked, "How long?" The old man said, "Oh, not for about ten seasons."

If propagandizing was being done in this village, it was being done by people of this very same tribe, and not by the Chinese. The Communists had frequently offered silver to young men and women of the tribes of Northern Laos and invited them to come to Yunnan and Canton. Here in the Chinese Communist states the people were gently but firmly and inexorably indoctrinated into the Communist belief. The communists dangled all sorts of glib allurements in front of these people and offered to them especially "progress." The young men and women believed with all their hearts that the new land reformers would offer something better to their backward villagers. They then returned to the village of their ancestors and became teachers, of untruths. To the ignorant people of their village they would say, "Let us build a school, for we know how to read and write and we wish you, our people, to know also." And the people wished for this knowledge and would cooperate.

These villagers have no concept of what happened in the political field. They have no idea of the rift the world has suffered. They understand nothing about the two camps of ideas, the God-loving men and the Godless men. They have no idea of what America is and certainly no idea of where it is located.

It is hard to make these people hate. It is the custom of the land that a stranger in the village must be well treated. We were usually met at the river's edge by some elder of the village with a small silver bowl containing some flowers, candles and other offerings of welcome to the visitors.

This little village was remarkable: it had sidewalks. It was the only village that I have seen in the Kingdom with sidewalks. Only here it was a centerwalk. The mud was so deep and so slippery in the monsoon rains, that the villagers had a raised path bordered on each side. Here caked mud and rocks a bit more solid were laid so that one could walk without slipping.

They found the spectacle of us Americans very interesting. They enjoyed watching us open our cans, cooking dinner, eating with bizarre instruments, mixing the black powder of Borden's, the white powder of Pream, the granules of sugar, and adding boiling water—these are strange-looking ceremonies to one who has never seen them before. To these villagers we were the greatest show on earth and the miraculousness of our medicines was most welcome. They had heard a little bit about us, and were very anxious to see us here in the flesh. Again many in this village seemed to have something wrong, but there were no psychosomatic diseases in Laos. For the record, during my year I never saw one case of neurosis.

According to the ancient map the halfway point for us would be the village of Nale. We arrived there in the late afternoon of the third day. This was not much different from other villages save it was a bit larger, and there was a police outpost there. Of course it was still raining when the village chief came out to welcome us. This man could read and write, and spoke some French, and had a fine substantial house. He had spent several years of his life in the capital of Vientiane, during the French occupation.

Next door to his home was a thatched sickbay with a "nurse" working there. This nurse had nothing in the way of medicines, not even aspirins, quinine or adhesive tape. He legally came under the Public Health Department of the Royal Kingdom but there was no way to get medicines to his outpost on anything like a regular schedule. The Royal Government was afraid to send any quantity of bulk medicines to this area for fear that it would fall into the hands of the bandits.

We had a long sick-call here lasting late into the night. There was a woman with a fibroid tumor; a boy with a type of ophthalmia which turns the eyeball into a whitish protruding globe; and several women with goiters; and one man here with a huge hernia.

We left many crates of medicines with the nurse, who seemed quite bright and very appreciative. I later told the Minister all about this.

The village chieftain gave us a fine little dinner mixed with our own food, and showed us then to the guest room. Because the advance *pirogue* of guards had told him we were coming, he had hastily constructed for the use of the white man some beds. "You know those bizarre white men do not sleep on stuffed leaf mats on the floor like normal people do. For some reason they put their mattresses up on a wooden frame and call it a bed." (Why do we?) He had had these beds constructed for us. But the measurements were a little off. They were only wide enough to lie perfectly still either on your back or on your stomach. If you rolled over, you would roll off for sure. Poor Bob with his husky six-foot frame really had a dangerous night.

We started up early the next day and several hours later we were overtaken by another *pirogue*. There was a frantic father in this boat who lived north of Nale. The night before, when we had arrived in Nale, his sister found out that we were the white doctors from Nam Tha. They had heard of us. She immediately set out by foot north to the village of her brother, and returned with him in the morning. They brought his dying daughter. We had already left the village so they borrowed a boat and came down to catch us.

We could not land anywhere because of the river and the jungle. He shot on down the rapids with us to the next village and carried his daughter into the guest hut. She had fulminating pneumonia. He respiration was already a death rattle. Her heartbeat was so faint that I could hardly hear it and her lips were blue from lack of oxygen. We did everything we could, gave her medicines and infusions, and finally turned to the father and offered him enough medicines to continue the treatment for several days. I knew that the treatment would be futile. I knew she could not possibly live. And she was only about three, the age of my own brother's daughter.

That night we spent in a Kha Kho village. It was an abhorrent little place where we were looked upon with real suspicion. Every child in that village had fulminating whooping cough. The night's air was torn by their hacking. We had plenty of terramycin which is specific against this organism, but the thick tenacious mucus clogging the throats of the children was the worst thing that I had ever seen. After a sleepless night, we packed up again. We loaded our gear, now considerably lighter, and continued on down the river. We stopped at several villages and around noon the sun came out. It was most welcome.

We went on down and reached the Mekong River by nightfall. At the village of Ban Pak Tha, the Nam Tha River weds the mighty Mekong. This is a fine old village built on a lush piece of land between the two rivers. It was small and of course very muddy, but it had something about it that was dignified.

The village chief took us to a big, decrepit, termite-infested house that had in former times been quite a beautiful place. It had belonged to the Provincial Governor. But years of monsoons, disuse and tropical ravages had nearly converted this to the dust from which it came. And the Governor had moved north to Nam Tha. However this house was the very best that he could offer to us and to our eyes it looked like Buckingham Palace. We held sick-call that night after dinner and it lasted until midnight. Kieu had come with us as interpreter for this trip. We sent Chai on to Vientiane by air, with all of the boys' baggage, as they were going to America at the end of this float. Their personal baggage was too valuable to risk on the river.

Kieu had been a good interpreter. I will never forget how he gently reprimanded me for riding a bicycle to the Governor's house one night in Nam Tha. It was only down the lane a bit and I did not feel like walking. I asked why in the world I should not ride a bike. He replied, *"Ce n'est pas chic."* He was awfully worried about "face"; apparently I did not think about it enough. John, with a Continental background, was much more aware of this sort of thing. John always knew the right words and never gave offense, whereas my hot Irish temper sometimes caused embarrassment.

This particular night I was tired and cross. The crowds at sick-call were doing what so frequently happens, they were closing in on me so tightly that I could hardly breathe, much less listen to a man's chest through a stethoscope. I instructed Kieu to tell them to move back as I was being suffocated. In his well-trained, gentlemanly manner, he said something. They did not move. I told him to get the mob back, I was getting a little frightened. He repeated something *sotto voce*. Finally I turned and yelled at him to tell the people to get back or I would stop sick-call. I had no idea that yelling at my interpreter would cause him to lose that much face. Kieu, being as tired and perhaps as cross as I was, just walked away and refused to work. John went to try to apologize for me and get him to come back, but he could not, for he would lose face. So we held sick-call without him. We were all under a terrible strain, even the Lao themselves. It is no wonder that we were all edgy, cross and irritable.

While we were bathing from a bucket of river water, eating our dinner, or holding sick-call, we would always be watched by that audience of people, hacking, spitting, and being sick at both ends. But their smiles were so gracious and they were so genuine that I could never get really angry with them.

Late that night after sick-call when we were so beat we could hardly hold our heads up, the village chief of Ban Pak Tha asked us to come to his house. We wanted to get out of it, but we went and were glad. We found that he had laid out a little private dinner for us. We had some good Lao soup, Lao alcohol, and for one of the few times in Asia, potatoes.

The next morning we changed boats. We were now nearing civilization, on the Mekong. Here there were larger boats that had motors on them. These haul rice up and down the wide river from Luang Prabang to Ban Pak Tha and then further up along the Burma border. We were able to get a place on one of these on top of several tons of burlap rice bags. We left all remaining medicines at Ban Pak Tha with the schoolteacher. Even the bags and the small black foot-locker in which we carried the supplies were left behind. With just our personal gear, plus a few gifts that were given to us, we left Ban Pak Tha for Luang Prabang.

These large motor-driven riverboats are built on Mississippi houseboat lines. Should we sit in the burlap on the main deck and slap at the bugs, or lie on the tin roof of the second deck and burn in the blazing sun? Being fair-skinned and having a certain amount of tolerance to fleas by this time, I took the lower berth, but the boys decided to go and sit on top and did get a good tan. I had had enough foresight to bring a book along, so sitting up on top of burlap bags, I read *The Great Alliance,* one of the volumes of Winston Churchill's history of the war. What more felicitous place in the wide world to read about our great ally England than on Asia's mighty Mekong?

On the afternoon of the eighth day we were still sprawled in confusion amidst the howling livestock, nursing mothers, sweating coolies, dried meats and other accoutrements of this Mekong *Queen Mary.* Kieu, now in better spirits, told us he had just heard the pilot say that we would soon be in Luang Prabang. We climbed out the side and up on the roof to watch beautiful, ancient Luang Prabang loom into view. The high golden spire of the main pagoda was the first thing that we saw. If it had been Paris in springtime or autumn in Manhattan, it could not have looked more beautiful to us.

As soon as the crew had a piece of planking down, we scrambled off the boat and climbed up the banks to the road. Here, with the solid earth beneath us, we felt that the river trip was at last completed. We felt as though the last days had been more fruitful than perhaps the whole preceding month. We really had taken American humanity into the most unknown, untouched hinterlands. We felt as though we had done some service in the name of our country, our fellow man and our God.

We grabbed two bicycle-propelled rickshaws and headed to the house of Dolf Droge, the head of USIS in Luang Prabang. When Dolf first looked at us, he said that we resembled prisoners who had just been released from Communism. But after a hot shower and a cold beer our looks were markedly improved, to say nothing of our spirits.

Although Vientiane is the administrative capital of Laos, Luang Prabang is the ancient religious capital. Here is the palace of the King. Here is where all the princes live and the court is held. We decided on our second afternoon to pay our respects to His Highness Prince Phetserath, the Viceroy of Laos. As the boys were going to fly on to Bangkok in a few days, we thought that this was the opportune time. We asked Dolf to come along with some camera equipment and get a few snapshots for us. This was especially interesting to Dolf, since Prince Phetserath has not always been interpreted as pro-American in his comments. Whatever may have been the Prince's political leanings, his social and native leanings were wonderful. He was genuinely interested in his people and he showed it. He had sent us a gift of some husky chickens of fine breed from Thailand.

We went to his palace which is beautifully situated, gardened and groomed on a bend of the river just outside Luang Prabang. We visited with His Royal Highness for an hour, during which time Dolf took some candid pictures. The Prince was tremendously interested in our river trip and in the sicknesses encountered. He then asked me about hospital problems, how much it was costing per patient for rice.

Dolf Droge, like his boss Hank Miller, is one of those excellent men who walk with kings and do not lose the common touch. Son of an immigrant who became a cowboy in Montana, Dolf has done all sorts of work from newspaper reporting to acting as a nightclub comedian. He stands over six-foot seven inches (Hank Miller being a mere six-foot-six). Dolf explained to the Prince that when he was in Thailand the people used to call him "Pret." The Prince knew the legend immediately. It seems that "Pret" of ancient Siam was a huge monster, larger than a coconut tree and just as thin. This monster would reach down and pick evil people up in his hands and devour them. I took the occasion to tell the Prince a little of my plans. I told him that my money was almost entirely exhausted now. My two assistants had to return to America because they would enter Notre Dame in the fall semester. This was already the month of August.

We explained that our locals had been well trained and that we hoped they would take over from us. I laughingly explained that I had come to give aid to the Lao and had succeeded in working myself out of a job. The Prince exclaimed, "Good!" When he saw my surprise at this he said, "This is what aid should be, doctor. It should not make the people more dependent upon the aider, or upon the country from which he has come. Aid should work itself into a position where it abolishes any further need of itself." After thinking about this, I agree.

We discussed some other ideas and he told me to see the Minister of Health and the Prime Minister when I returned to Vientiane. We intended to fly down on the Veha Akhat's small plane the following day. The two boys would leave in a few days for Bangkok and then on back to the States. I would call upon the Ministers.

As we left, the Prince walked out of his palace and down to the jeep with us. He turned to us, holding out his hand in democratic fashion, and said, "Thank you for what you have done for my people, and come back again."

11

The Minister Agrees

We arrived in Vientiane in early August. John and Bob since February had been living in Nam Tha, with only a rare break from their work. And they had done an excellent job. With no previous medical training, they had not thought that they would ever be able to learn the things they had to know. Very little time elapsed before they had accomplished extraordinary tasks. Pain, hunger, ignorance, these are the things that go on forever, and these are the greatest internationalists of them all. These are the things which Americans are so well armed to fight against. Gentleness, intelligence and will can conquer. My boys illustrated this. And in this conquest John and Bob felt the vivid and intense joy of being able to serve. The best thing I can say of them is that they are fine Americans. I am proud to have had them on my team.

After they flew out of Vientiane, I was alone. But the job was not quite completed. I went to see the Minister of Health to present my "phase-out" plan. I had prepared a schedule, and intended to offer my proposals, and to make a request. I wanted the continuity of my program guaranteed. We had established the hospital at Nam Tha, and wanted to insure that after our departure it would continue to flourish. All the things we had done were so carried out that our departure would not create a void. We installed no X-ray machines, nor any large electrical plant. We had no complicated or extremely delicate instruments. We utilized ten or twelve basic antibiotics and other medicines, so that their exact usage and dosage was well understood by the local nurses. We turned over to midwives the CARE kits making them completely self-sufficient. The vaccination program, carried out by the locals themselves, would add a marked degree of immunity to many thousands of people in the high valley. The instructions would make them more cognizant of the relationships between dirt and disease. I did not want these accomplishments lost after our departure. I wanted to make sure that we would leave something real and substantial behind us.

I proposed three points to the Minister. I asked first, that he give our hospital a charter. This would mean that a specific amount of money would be earmarked for the hospital based on the number of patients treated, and hospitalized. This would mean that certain monies would be allotted for upkeep, and care of the buildings. Instead of paint and wood being bought with my own money, the hospital would now be administered and financed by the government of Laos, and their medicines would come from the government warehouse.

Second, I asked that he send to Nam Tha two Bangkok-trained nurses to replace my men. These nurses were well trained in Thailand's school of nursing. There were only a few in the whole Kingdom of Laos, but I asked for two for Nam Tha.

Third, I asked that a *médecin indochinois* be sent to replace me. There are no other doctors by international standards in the kingdom, except the Minister himself. There are 15 men who have had some medical training, though by our standards very little. These men could practice medicine in Laos.

If Dr. Oudom, the Minister of Health would agree to this, I in turn would agree to leave everything that we had brought to Laos in the hospital at Nam Tha. This meant that absolutely everything would stay there, beds, mosquito nets, linens, drapes, surgical instruments, stethoscopes, otoscopes, house gear, and about $25,000 worth of antibiotics. All these we would turn over to the *médecin indochinois*. Then I would myself return to America.

The Minister immediately agreed, but expressed some surprise that I wanted to become expendable. I told him that in my mind America should not attempt to build a dynasty in a foreign land. We should not attempt to make a foreign land dependent on us for its maintenance.

Dr. Oudom was pleased with this point of view. I also remembered the rapidity with which Prince Phetsareth had said "Good" when I told him that I had worked myself out of a job. The Minister asked, "Are you content to be replaced by a man who does not measure up to your ability as a physician?" I said that I believed the *médecin indochinois* to be the best that the Lao government had in the medical program, and that I would be very pleased if he would take over what we had built. I felt that if I had closed down the hospital at my departure, this would have intimated that no one else could do the job as well as we could.

Guardedly I added, "I hope you are not too pleased with my departure because I hope to return to Laos again."

With a smile, Dr. Oudom said: "You and your men have had the cotton strings of *baci* tied on your arms, and the heart of the Lao put in your hands. You may return whenever you wish."

I left to return to the north for a six weeks' phase-out period. The plane was forced down in Luang Prabang for several days, but when the rains lessened a bit in their fury, I was able to get on up to Nam Tha.

Most of the village met the plane, and all were relieved to know we had completed the great float without mishap. They also noted that the cast I had been wearing for so long was now off my wrist. They were not nearly as pleased as I was. Now I was a little more mobile, and could do surgery again.

Si was glad to be back in his domain in our kitchen again, but felt as though his job as a cook had shrunk to almost nothing. All he had to do was feed me. And our hut of a house seemed enormous. I was entirely alone, and rattled around in the place as though it was a huge barn. The new "doctor," who had just arrived, was going to move into my house and I intended to fulfill my promise of leaving everything for him. For the present time, however, he lived in the house of the Chao Khuong.

I explained to him how we had urged our patients to pay us for our medicines. I believed this important for two reasons. First of all, we needed the food; running and stocking the hospital was expensive enough without having to go to the village markets and buy chickens and eggs. Secondly, Operation Laos was not supposed to be a charity program. We were not here for hand-outs. The people of Laos are proud, and were pleased to pay for what we offered to them. This increased their prestige and mine too. One of the most touching of these payments was a gift that an old Yao once gave me. It was a small towel that she had found somewhere. She had embroidered with her home-grown cotton thread the words in Chinese characters for "A Cheery Good Morning".

The Lao doctor agreed about "fees" and said he would continue it. One of the first things he did was to start the villagers building a large fence around the hospital compound. This would keep the water buffalo from meandering around the front lawn of the surgical ward. I wondered why I had never thought of it.

This young doctor had had his *lycée* graduation in Vientiane. He then went to a "medical school" for two years in Cambodia, and became a "doctor". He was very young, very bright and anxious to please and impress all about him. He was typical of the new generation of Asia complete with wrist watch, expensive shoes, and high ideals. Yet he still respected the words of his grandfather with childlike humility.

We spent many hours together going over the medicines and instruments. I taught him how to run the sterilizer and how to put up surgical packs and instrument kits. He assisted me in a lot of surgery himself, with Lao nurses and midwives working as scrub and circulating nurses. He was conscious of his new duties and took them very seriously. He ran the sick-call line every day and I would go over just before noon to see certain cases upon which he wished to have my opinion. Then in the afternoons we would do surgery.

All the villagers knew that the new Lao doctor was replacing me, and the two new nurses were the replacements for John and Bob. Whenever they expressed fear, we tried to transfer to the Lao doctor all allegiance that we had won from a year in this country. He would need it.

The governor gave a going-away party for me with all the village in attendance. A Lam Vong, the national dance of Laos, was held. We had done it frequently; in fact, Pete and John were quite expert at it. I was sorry they were not with me that night in September.

A platform was built in the village square, and the amplifier from our movie projector was used for the local orchestra of drums, khenes, and string instruments. The dancers all lined up but did not touch each other. Placed side by side they moved rhythmically around in a large circle. They twisted their arms and hands with great delicacy. The dancers become experts in keeping masklike faces, while weaving around the dance floor. During the previous year, whenever a Lam Vong was held, you could always find a member of the Dooley mission there. Tonight I was alone.

Every day villagers and mountain tribesmen would come to my house and give me going-away gifts. They would sit and chat about this or that, ask me how far it was to my village in America, and when would I return to Nam Tha. I knew they were sorry to see me go. The children would laugh a little, and I kept up "face". Even in the depths of their misery the children seemed always to manage a little laugh.

The Asian smile is more overwhelming than anywhere else. The Asian uses his smile as the mask or the mirror of his heart. Anger, fear, hurt, apprehension, these can all be manifested with a smile. I have seen the Asian smiling to explain how something pains him. I have seen the Asian smiling when he knows he will soon be operated on. I have seen the Asian smiling when he fears what the spirits or the white medicine man will do next.

The old witch doctors came to say goodbye. The teller of old legends, tales of love and sweet grief, he too came and wished me all happiness. He said that he hoped a butterfly would perch on my shoulder and that this good omen would bring me happiness. An old sorcerer came and sat before me and shook her joss sticks in their cylinders. She threw the half-moon clappers on the ground before me and said that my future looked bright, and in it she could see my return to her village. As she left, she fell into a spasm of coughing; the agony of rampaging tuberculosis.

Now that the boys were gone, my life was desperately singular. I used to look in the mirror and talk to myself just to hear English: "Good morning, Dooley, you look like the devil today." Si and Chai knew my loneliness and would come and sit at the table with me during meals. We spoke of our plans. I had found jobs for them in the American community down in Vientiane. They would work there until I returned. And my own plans—simple.

I wanted to tell America about Laos, and to point out the fact that we can span the gap between nations with a bridge whose fibers are woven of compassion. Someone had written to me and said that I must feel awfully limited in my work in Laos—limited by lack of transportation and communication, by custom and isolation. He wrote: "Give me a wider horizon." I wanted to show how vast the horizons of the spirit can be. And especially I wanted to show that we Americans possess an instrument not too well developed, more powerful than any bomb yet devised. It is the force that can relieve ugliness and tragedy. It is the force of gentleness.

On the morning of my departure hundreds upon hundreds of villagers were milling around the strip when I walked out with Si and Chai. How different these people seemed now—from the preceding February when we first walked down this lane from the landing strip. Now I knew each one, remembered their suffering, had lived part of their life, had become involved in some portion of their existence. As I walked through the crowd many reached out and thanked me with the simple eloquence of a touch.

I felt some guilt in leaving, but some pride in knowing that there was now a hospital in Nam Tha and things would run well. Strangely enough, these people had become important to me. I had learned to love them.

The plane took off. In the air the French pilot, usually untouched by the peasantry of the north, turned and said to me, *"Ils vous aiment bien."* Yes, I believe they did love me too.

12

Sunlight on the Edge

As the plane flew quietly on south to Vientiane, I thought of the thousands of hours I had spent in these villages. I remembered the long talks with the ancient old folk, many who seemed to be Father Asia personified—Ojisan, Old Joe, Maggie, the Chao Khuong, Cauvin. I looked at Chai and Si cramped in the small back seat and the words of James Michener came to my mind. I had read them long ago, and now the sentences took on a muscle and flesh, a hue and tone. They were applicable here with astonishing accuracy. He wrote:

"Most people in Asia will go to bed hungry tonight.

Most people in Asia live in grinding poverty.

Most people in Asia have never seen a doctor.

Most people in Asia believe anything different would be better than what they have, and they are determined to get it.

Most people in Asia have never known civil liberties.

Most people in Asia believe that freedom of enterprise means the right of the Western Colonial powers to exploit them.

Most people in Asia distrust people with white skins.

Most people in Asia are determined never again to be ruled by foreigners."

Many say that, until the villagers learn to read and write, democracy can never exist in Asia. They say that the masses of the peoples, the land people, are really not a power in Asia. Perhaps villagers do not wax eloquent on political affairs, but let their personal lives be affected to their dislike, and they will speak with massive action. An example is the exodus of nearly a million North Vietnamese to the south, for one reason: people did not wish to live under a political rule that was godless. Perhaps their own inaction, coupled with the white man's errors, helped to bring this ogre to their land. But they have action now. There is great conflict now, and there are many errors. Perhaps there will be greater anguish in the future. But these are the birth pains of freedom.

139

Suddenly the little plane pitched into a steep bank and circled the airstrip at Vientiane. Down and down it flew, then we hit the runway with a gentle bump, a bounce, and the softer bump of the tail wheel. There was a rumbling race along the runway, an awkward turn, and we taxied to the parking area. I was back in Vientiane for a goodbye.

I went to pay my respects to Ambassador Parsons, who wished me all success in my hopes for return. I visited the administrators of the economic aid program. I felt that now I had much more insight into the situation than before. It is trite to reiterate that economic aid is essential to the life of Laos. But what should we expect in return? Their alliance, their friendship, their adherence to our policies? If the Lao government does not always follow the "American Line," let us not immediately attack them. Asian nations, newly independent and fiercely proud, will never accept any kind of American domination, however benevolent our intentions may be.

When a man chooses to "do good" in this world, it has been said that he cannot expect other men to roll boulders off his path. On the contrary, he can expect some people to roll them on it.

There is a glaring contrast in the yet underdeveloped Asia. One sees beauty and decay, and at the same time a massive potential for a new and throbbing life. Amidst the beauty there is horror, and the constant stalking threat of Communist conquest.

Many Americans are working in Asia to prevent this conquest. Most Americans are doing a superb job, yet there are great errors, easy to see. The most devastating is an attitude, held by some, that, simply because people in Laos live close to the earth, away from traffic, smoke, miltown, and cocktails, they are therefore *ad hoc* healthy and happy. "Don't change them, they're happy in their ignorance." "Why show them what they can never achieve themselves?" "They don't want to advance, they are perfectly unruffled and content." This pseudo-sophisticated attitude is not only wrong, it is malicious.

Let us stop all this blather and bleat about the beatitudes of democracy. Let us get out and show, with simple spontaneity and love, our ability to work at the level of the people we aim to aid. Let us stop proclaiming ourselves as the world standard. Democracy, as championed by the United States, does not translate well into Lao. Not yet. We evolved it from 1776 to 1958. Let us be patient with the Asian. The Lao need only time, education, and stimulation.

I believe that we would gain more for our own country (and this is certainly part of the incentive behind our foreign aid) if we emphasized the connections that exist between peoples. Let us show that we believe these connections to be greater than the differences. The cables binding humanity around the world are stronger than national rivalries. Let us re-affirm, and then live, our belief in the family of man. Let us prove again that America understands that "God hath made of one blood all men for to dwell upon the earth."

I said goodbye to the Ministers and restated my desire to return. They said that my mission would always be welcome, no matter what the political circumstances. To Chai and Si I offered my sincere thanks for their aid and fellowship. And on the third day I slipped out to the airfield for the flight to Bangkok. In Bangkok I changed to the huge plane and within a few hours of my departure I was listening to the clipped, precise English of the PAA stewardess. Her words sounded almost foreign to my ears.

As the plane lunged through the night, I reviewed what had passed through the turbulent fifteen months. Suddenly a little ray of morning came across the sky and I saw some sunlight on the edge of tomorrow. I said a prayer of thanks to God. I used to be selfish in my prayers, always asking for something. This prayer was different. I am now tremendously aware of my gratitude to Him.

I was back in America last November when the news broke that the Royal Government had settled its differences with the "dissident brothers" of northern Laos. A new coalition government was formed with two cabinet posts going to the Pathet Lao, including Prince SouphanouVong as Minister of Reconstruction and Town Planning. The Prince disavowed his allegiance to Communism, and denied that he was unfriendly to the West. Still, there were skeptics who said that the move marked the beginning of Communist infiltration. Who knows? Certainly not I.

Laos was still first on my own order of unfinished business. I was in Washington to meet for the first time a man who had been my most sympathetic and inspiring correspondent for nearly a year. He was Dr. Peter Commanduras, a distinguished Washington physician and associate professor of

Clinical Medicine at the George Washington University Medical School.

We met in the lobby of the Mayflower Hotel and went in to luncheon. Dr. Commanduras was a handsome, dignified man in his early 50s, with a youthful face topped by greying hair. As we talked through luncheon, I began to understand his interest in my work. His clear concept of American medical aid to foreign countries, independent of government control and performed by individual doctors, went far beyond my own thinking.

Dr. Commanduras had tried and failed to sell his commonsense approach to foreign-aid officials who are impatient with anything less than multi-million dollar projects. Like me, he advocated keeping things simple, making a modest start, building slowly. He was delighted when I produced figures to show that our sixteen months' mission had cost less than $50,000 plus the contributions of pharmaceuticals and supplies.

But he also had what I lacked—the experience, temperament and ability to plan and direct operations. I see myself as just another worker in the vineyard. Hence his next remark took me completely by surprise.

"I have been thinking seriously of taking up this work myself," he said. "My children are about through college, the family is fairly well provided for, my wife goes along wholeheartedly with my ideas." He paused for a moment, and then looked at me with a twinkle in his eyes. "I feel pretty much as you do, Dooley," he said. "How can we go around preaching this idea to others unless we're willing to practice it ourselves?"

One week later I stood in the board room of the International Rescue Committee and faced the distinguished group of directors seated around the big table. Leo Cherne, the chairman, introduced me and asked me to tell my story. When I had finished with my report on Operation Laos, I sat down and waited.

"Well, doctor," someone asked, "what do you have to propose?"

"From the modest beginning I have made," I said, "I propose that we carry the work another step forward. I believe I have demonstrated that a medical team like mine can be kept in the field for sixteen months on a budget of $50,000. Dr. Commanduras and I have drawn up a plan for sending out six such teams. My team will return to Laos, the other five can be sent into other critical areas. I propose that our plan be adopted and sponsored by the International Rescue Committee."

There was silence. I sat down and waited for discussion.

Angier Biddle Duke, president of the International Rescue Committee, said: "The IRC has previously helped refugees from totalitarian oppression. Under the proposed medical program we can help a different kind of refugee, refugees from pain, from wretchedness, from misery, refugees in their own country."

Most of the board members agreed that this concept of humanitarian work, free from the stigma of proselytizing or policy peddling, was indeed a fine thing. But apparently the program was not consistent with the traditional approach of IRC, for someone then said: "We'll have to change the charter, but it's not that easy."

Well, I thought, *Bau pinh yanh,* as we say in Lao.

"Why not?" I blithely asked.

They all laughed good-naturedly at my brashness and naïveté, and then began to discuss the point. Then suddenly a motion was made to amend the charter enabling us to "accept the task of providing humanitarian medical aid to threatened parts of the world." The motion was seconded, and passed by a unanimous vote. I felt like swooning in my leather-cushioned chair.

That was the birth of MEDICO—officially Medical International Cooperation, a division of the International Rescue Committee. Dr. Gordon Seagrave, the world famous Burma Surgeon, will head up the work in Burma. Early this summer I will be on my way back to Laos. The four other teams are being shaped up under the direction of Dr. Commanduras. We already have a great many volunteers—doctors and dentists who are ready to sacrifice their practices; nurses, technicians, social workers, and plain college students like John deVitry and Bob Waters who are eager to serve on the teams.

The medical profession has rallied to our support. There's a plan afoot for a roving team of medical specialists—an eye man, an obstetrician, an orthopedic surgeon, a tropical medicine expert, etc.—who will rotate among the MEDICO outposts, treating patients and teaching native doctors and nurses.

MEDICO won't be big or fancy. (The global planners will probably sneer at us as pretty small potatoes.) But we'll be doctors doing what God meant us to do—treating sick people, and probably some of the most desperately sick people in the world.

We will do our level best, wherever we go, and with what little we have, to let the plain people of the world know that Americans really care.

At this juncture I thought of Dr. Schweitzer. I wrote at once and told him of our program, our high hopes, our belief that Americans would back us with the help we needed. MEDICO'S teams can only be the hands; the heart is always in America. I pointed out that through MEDICO Americans could show to the world not only how Americans will care for and help other men, but how men can care for and help other men.

I asked that he accept a position such as he has never before accepted in his eighty-four years. The warmest and proudest statement we can make is that Dr. Albert Schweitzer has accepted the position of Honorary Patron of MEDICO.

With those who have helped us in the past, and with those who will work on and support MEDICO teams in the future, I wish to share these words I received in a letter from Dr. Schweitzer:

"I do not know what your destiny will ever be, but this I do know . . . You will always have happiness if you seek and find: how to serve."